Topics in the Biology of Aging

Symposium on Topics in the Biology of Aging

Topics in the Biology of Aging

A Symposium Held at
The Salk Institute for Biological Studies,
San Diego, California, November 4-6, 1965
Under Contract with the Aging Program of the
National Institute of Child Health and Human Development
U.S. Public Health Service

Edited by

Peter L. Krohn

University of Birmingham

Interscience Publishers
a division of John Wiley & Sons
New York · London · Sydney

Preface

This is the first of a series of monographs from The Salk Institute for Biological Studies. The papers which are published here were presented at a Symposium on Topics in the Biology of Aging held at the Institute in San Diego, California, on November 4, 5, and 6, 1965. The Symposium was held by The Salk Institute under contract with the Aging Program of the National Institute of Child Health and Human Development, U.S. Public Health Service.

The Symposium was essentially a research meeting to examine and evaluate some of the most recent work on the biology of aging. Among the subjects covered by the speakers were aging of microorganisms and insects; radiation damage, chromosome breakage and aging; aging of cells in tissue culture; aging and tissue transplantation; and the molecular biology of aging.

Dr. Leslie E. Orgel, Senior Fellow at The Salk Institute, and Dr. James Birren, former Director, Aging Program, National Institute of Child Health and Human Development and now Director, Rossmoor-Cortese Institute for the Study of Retirement and Aging, University of Southern California, were responsible for the program. They were assisted by Dr. Peter Krohn, School of Medicine, University of Birmingham, Birmingham, England, who helped in the planning and who has also edited the proceedings, and by Mr. William Glazier of The Salk Institute, who handled the arrangements for the Symposium and for this publication.

Leo Szilard (1898—1964)

It is appropriate that this record of a Symposium on Aging should be opened by a brief mention of Leo Szilard and his work. For the conference itself owed much to him in two different ways. First, he was one of the moving spirits who helped to conceive the idea of the Institute and to bring it into being. Second, he was especially interested in the problems of Aging, and the idea of having the conference was very much linked with his name. It is sad that he did not live to take part in a meeting to which he would have added not only light but wit.

Szilard came out of that extraordinary uprush of educational inspiration in Hungary that followed the separation from the Austrian Empire just after 1918–19, when many bright men who previously had been excluded were for the first time able to be educated. It is interesting to recall that his first very important piece of work—now almost forgotten—was on thermodynamic processes in general and how they relate to the function of the brain. In it he set up for the first time the idea that the brain creates information by sacrificing entropy, which is essentially the leading idea that was rediscovered in much more specific terms by Shannon and others 20 years later. He developed, of course, into a foremost nuclear physicist and was the author of the famous letter to President Roosevelt which was signed by Einstein.

But after the War he decided to learn biology. Indeed, it was a characteristic of his to leave behind a field of interest after a number of years and move away into another one. "Do your work for six years; but in the seventh, go into solitude or among strangers, so that the memory of your friends does not hinder you from being what you have become," is what he said in prefatory remarks to a German edition of *The Voice of the Dolphins*. In each new field he would assimilate all the available information and reassemble it into striking new forms of thought.

Some minds convert detail to principles quickly while others move ponderously, defending all the way what earlier was believed to be true. Szilard wanted merely to know the facts which he then soon assembled into new forms of thought. This capacity to perceive the essence of things and to see and formulate fundamental principles was the nature of his wisdom.

The new patterns he laid down were no doubt wrong in detail and he never had time to work things through to a conclusion before he was off on another chase to revivify a new subject with fresh ideas. To comment that he started something and did not always himself bring it to completion is to praise him for moving on when he had carried something as far as he could alone or with the resources then available. He was, indeed, the rare prophet who did not stop to do battle in ways that would spend his creative energy wastefully.

Above all Szilard was a devoted scientist who abhorred an approach to science that he considered irresponsible. He was dedicated, too, to the problems of mankind. So he was a politically conscious scientist who was motivated towards the relief of human suffering and a humanist with a powerful intellect. It was not his intellect alone that was so rare but the combination of qualities that he possessed.

His interests in fields of biology ranged from the most abstract to the exceedingly practical but were usually not in phenomena for themselves. He was concerned either for their bearing on the basic understanding of related phenomena or for a directly practical aim. The same sense of responsibility he showed in public affairs guided his approach to biological problems--to ferret out the essential phenomena and to put them into an orderly theory, to make alternative theories and to test them. Experiments just to see what happens and not to distinguish sharply two alternative hypotheses were of no interest to him.

The areas in which he focused his attention were wide, and included the biological effects of irradiation, genetics, regulation of protein formation in bacteria and in embryogenesis, problems and mechanisms of population control, phenomena of immunology, and those of memory and recall.

Everyone at the Symposium must have been influenced by Szilard's contribution to our understanding of the mechanisms by which an organism ages and eventually dies. The physiological age of an individual reflects, he thought, the proportion of the chromosome controlled synthetic machinery of the cells which has been lost. Characteristically, his ideas probably represent no more than a partial truth, but they have served to stimulate, excite, and irritate other people to do experiments.

But the real evidence for his effect on biology is not to be found in his published papers. It lies hidden in the papers of so many other people who benefited by his intense curiosity and analytical mind. One would have to know which conferences he attended and also which ones he refused to attend; which papers he listened to, which he slept through, and which he only seemed to sleep through, for he had a disturbing habit of seeming to awaken to ask embarrassing questions.

Szilard frequently amused himself and everyone else by inventing ways to make research conferences less fatiguing in order to leave more time for leisurely discussion and the real exchange of ideas. Of the many possible devices none was so clever as the one in which he proposed that each speaker should stand and briefly state only the conclusion of his experiments or thoughts. If they were easily understood and credible, no one would need to ask for evidence and time would be saved. If they were not, the cross-examination could start.

If we had followed the "Szilard Rule" during this Symposium, one of us would have stood up to say, "Leo Szilard was a brilliantly imaginative man who enjoyed thinking and who made everyone around him think, and he was a responsible, warm human being who made everyone around him responsible and warm." Then the speaker could have sat down—and there would have been no questions asked.

Symposium Participants

DR. K. C. ATWOOD, *University of Illinois*
DR. J. E. BIRREN, *University of Southern California*
DR. G. H. BOURNE, *Emory University*
DR. D. BRANDES, *Johns Hopkins Hospital*
DR. J. BRONOWSKI, *Harvard University*
DR. R. S. CHANG, *Salk Institute*
DR. I. CRAWFORD, *Scripps Clinic and Research Foundation*
DR. H. J. CURTIS, *Brookhaven National Laboratories*
DR. R. DULBECCO, *Salk Institute*
DR. L. E. DUNCAN, *National Institutes of Health*
DR. P. M. GALLOP, *Yeshiva University*
DR. D. A. GLASER, *University of California, Berkeley*
DR. C. GROBSTEIN, *University of California, San Diego*
DR. J. GROSS, *Harvard Medical School*
DR. A. B. HASTINGS, *Scripps Clinic and Research Foundation*
DR. L. HAYFLICK, *University of Pennsylvania*
DR. O. KAPLAN, *San Diego State College*
DR. R. R. KOHN, *Western Reserve University*
DR. P. L. KROHN, *University of Birmingham, England*
DR. E. LENNOX, *Salk Institute*
DR. J. MAYNARD SMITH, *University of Sussex, England*
DR. P. B. MEDAWAR, *National Institute of Medical Research, England*
DR. S. MILLS, *University of California, San Diego*
DR. L. ORGEL, *Salk Institute*
DR. M. POLLOCK, *Scripps Clinic and Research Foundation*
DR. T. T. PUCK, *University of Colorado*
DR. M. ROCKSTEIN, *University of Miami*
DR. D. RUBINSTEIN, *Veterans Administration Hospital, Baltimore*
DR. J. SALK, *Salk Institute*
DR. B. SALLMAN, *University of Miami*
DR. J. W. SAUNDERS, JR., *Marquette University*
DR. G. SCHAISBERGER, *University of Miami*
DR. F. M. SINEX, *Boston University*

DR. J. SPIZIZEN, *Scripps Clinic and Research Foundation*
DR. H. STERN, *University of California, San Diego*
DR. B. L. STREHLER, *Veterans Administration Hospital, Baltimore*
DR. L. C. STRONG, *Salk Institute*
DR. J. TILL, *Ontario Cancer Institute, Canada*
DR. M. VOGT, *Salk Institute*
DR. R. L. WALFORD, *University of California, Los Angeles*
DR. C. M. WILLIAMS, *Harvard University*
DR. V. J. WULFF, *Masonic Medical Research Laboratory*
DR. F. YOUNG, *Scripps Clinic and Research Foundation*

Contents

J. Maynard Smith: THEORIES OF AGING   1

DISCUSSION: *Atwood, Birren, Bourne, Curtis, Dulbecco, Glaser, Grobstein, Gross, Kohn, Maynard Smith, Medawar, Rockstein, Sinex, Wulff*   27

D. A. Glaser: AGING OF MICROORGANISMS (Summary)   37

DISCUSSION: *Glaser, Kohn, Maynard Smith, Medawar, Orgel, Puck, Sallman, Williams*   38

M. Rockstein: BIOLOGY OF AGING IN INSECTS . . .   43

DISCUSSION: *Birren, Bourne, Kohn, Maynard Smith, Orgel, Rockstein, Salk, Sallman, Sinex*   60

H. J. Curtis: THE ROLE OF SOMATIC MUTATIONS IN AGING   63

DISCUSSION: *Atwood, Brandes, Bronowski, Curtis, Dulbecco, Hastings, Kohn, Krohn, Maynard Smith, Orgel, Puck, Rubenstein, Sallman, Sinex, Stern, Till, Vogt, Walford, Williams*   74

L. Hayflick: CELL CULTURE AND THE AGING PHENOMENON   83

T. T. Puck, C. A. Waldren, and J. H. Tjio: SOME DATA BEARING ON THE LONG TERM GROWTH OF MAMMALIAN CELLS *IN VITRO*   101

DISCUSSION: *Atwood, Curtis, Dulbecco, Gallop, Glaser, Grobstein, Hayflick, Kohn, Maynard Smith, Medawar, Orgel, Puck, Strehler, Till, Williams, Wulff*   117

P. L. Krohn: TRANSPLANTATION AND AGING . . .   125

DISCUSSION: *Bourne, Bronowski, Curtis, Glaser Gross, Hayflick, Kohn, Krohn, Medawar, Rockstein, Strehler, Strong, Walford*   139

D. Brandes: LYSOSOMES AND AGING PIGMENT . . .   149

DISCUSSION: *Bourne, Kohn, Orgel, Strehler, Till*   157

J. W. Saunders, Jr.: CELL DEATH IN EMBRYOS:
ACCELERATED SENESCENCE? 159

DISCUSSION: *Grobstein, Medawar, Saunders* 161

R. L. Walford: GENERALIZING BIOLOGIC HYPOTHESES
AND AGING: AN IMMUNOLOGICAL APPROACH 163

DISCUSSION: *Kohn, Maynard Smith, Medawar, Walford* . . . 169

AUTHOR INDEX 171

SUBJECT INDEX 175

THEORIES OF AGING

J. Maynard Smith

School of Biological Sciences,
University of Sussex,
Brighton, England

INTRODUCTION

My purpose is not to summarize what is known about aging, but to consider some possible theories of aging, and some of the evidence for and against them. But even in this more modest aim I have had to be selective. In making this selection I have been guided by four convictions, or perhaps by four prejudices. The first three of these convictions may seem idiosyncratic; they are that it is impossible to think clearly about aging without at the same time thinking about natural selection; that there is no such thing as *the* aging process, only a number of different aging processes; and that although a number of different processes may be important in aging, somatic mutation is probably not one of them. My fourth conviction is in one sense almost universal among biologists—it is that my own work is more interesting than other people's. I shall therefore spend a quite unjustified proportion of my time discussing aging in insects.

But first I must offer some definition of aging and discuss how its occurrence is to be measured. As an aging process I mean any process occurring in an individual which renders that individual more likely to die in a given time interval as it grows older. In other words, an aging process is one which causes an increase in the force of mortality with age.

There are in effect two ways of demonstrating that aging occurs in a given species. One is to measure particular physiological functions in individuals of different ages, or still better, in the same individual at different ages. Thus if a man's speed over 100 yards was measured annually from the age of 30 onwards, it would be found to decline, gradually at first and then more steeply. In an environment in which lions or motor-buses were an important cause of death, this decline in speed would be an aging process by the definition given above.

1

A second method is to measure the force of mortality in a population. If the force of mortality increases with age, and provided there are no reasons to think that old individuals are being exposed to more severe conditions than young ones, then aging processes must be occurring. Figure 1 shows examples of these two methods for male drosophila. The first important point to be made is that it is impossible to deduce from the shape of a life table anything about the shape of the curve of physiological function against age. A life table—whether it be plotted as in Figure 1, or as log N against t (in which case a population with a constant force of mortality will give a straight line), or as a "Gompertz plot" of the logarithm of the force of mortality against age (which has been found to give an approximately straight line for a number of populations) —provides information about differences in age at death between members of a population. These differences are due either to genetic differences between members of the population, or to differences between the environmental circumstances met by them, or perhaps to differences in the incidence of random events in the lifetime of different individuals. Hence the shape of a life table may tell us something about the range of genetic variation in the population, or about the range of environmental circumstances or the incidence of random events; but it can tell us nothing about the relative rate of aging processes in the same individual at different ages.

Although both methods demonstrate the occurrence of aging processes, they do not measure the same thing. A life table gives a crude measure of the sum total of all aging processes occurring, whereas the physiological approach gives a more precise picture of particular aging processes.

AGING, NATURAL SELECTION, AND IMMORTALITY

We might expect organisms to age for much the same reason that we expect complex machines like motorcars and typewriters to age. For any object which is both complicated and well adapted, either for survival or for the performance of some particular function, most changes occurring either as a result of use or accident are likely to reduce that adaptation. The accumulation of such changes will finally result in the death of the organism, or, in the case of a machine, in complete loss of function. Thus to paraphrase Gibbon, what requires an explanation is not that organisms age, but that they last so long.

This conclusion is not invalidated by the fact that living organisms have self-repairing mechanisms, since these mechanisms themselves

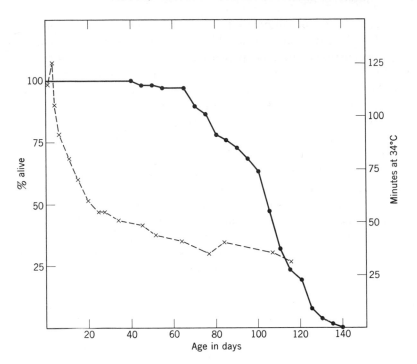

Fig. 1. Two methods of measuring aging in male *Drosophila subobscura* (data from Hollingsworth & Bowler 1966): Full line, % of survivors; broken line, mean survival time in minutes at 34° C in dry air.

must ultimately wear out. But the potential immortality of populations of animals and plants suggests that organisms too might be potentially immortal, since organisms are populations of cells. Populations which are potentially immortal, however, consist of entities with the properties of multiplication, heredity, and variation. Such populations survive because natural selection can eliminate inadaptive changes, but they inevitably undergo evolutionary change. In other words, natural selection between cells does not provide a method of producing an organism which is at the same time unchanging and potentially immortal.

But it is perhaps worth pointing out that a machine could in principle be designed (or an organism could in principle evolve) which was at the same time immortal and unchanging, and which required only an unpatterned input of energy. Suppose a machine carried with it a set of instructions by which it could be made, and that machine and instructions were compared at regular intervals, the machine on each occasion being corrected to agree with the instructions. Then provided that the instructions could be prevented from changing, the machine would be immortal. Now an unchanging set of instructions could be produced by the same techniques as are used in the construction of error-correcting codes used to feed information into computers. A simple but rather inefficient procedure would be to start with three identical sets of instructions, compare them with each other at regular intervals, and at each point where there was a disagreement take a "majority vote"; i.e., if one set of instructions differed from the other two it would be altered to agree with them. By increasing the number of replicates and the frequency of comparison, the probability of an error arising and being perpetuated could be reduced below any specified level.

There is at present little reason to think that such methods of error correction have been adopted by living organisms, either to ensure a longer life or to reduce the genetic mutation rate. But so long as a large part of the DNA in the nuclei of higher organisms is unexplained the possibility should be borne in mind.

If it is accepted that aging is an expected property of muticellular organisms, there is no need to suggest that it has evolved because it has been favored by natural selection. The relevance of natural selection to a causal analysis of aging arises for a different reason (Medawar 1952, Williams 1957, Maynard Smith 1962) ; natural selection will tend to synchronize different aging processes, even if these are physiologically independent. Suppose that in a particular natural population, one particular aging process—for example, atherosclerosis —proceeded much more rapidly than any other, so that any increase in the force of mortality with age occurred from this cause. Then any genetic change tending to delay the onset of atherosclerosis would be favored by selection, whereas genetic changes tending to cause an earlier onset of other aging changes would not be selected against. The result of such selection would be the synchrony of physiologically independent aging changes.

Synchrony of different aging changes could also be caused by physiological interdependence. Therefore to demonstrate that synchronizing selection has in fact been effective requires the identification of physiologically independent aging processes. One such process is the mechanical wearing away of the teeth in herbivorous mammals. The teeth of mice, horses, and elephants each last approximately as long as the rest of the animal, and this can only be the result of synchronizing selection. To give a more sophisticated example, Krohn (1962) has shown by transplanting ovaries between young and old mice that the ovaries age autonomously. If the same is true of other mammals, then the approximate synchrony between the decline in fertility and other aging changes is also the consequence of selection.

It therefore seems quite likely that in any species a number of different aging processes occur which are independent in the sense that each would continue, perhaps at an altered rate, even if the others were prevented. This I shall call the theory that aging is "multiple," as opposed to the view that all or most of the symptoms of old age are consequences of some single aging process. If aging is multiple, it will prove very difficult to achieve a significant prolongation of human life, because this will require the arresting not of one but of many processes. More immediately, it means that in most arguments about the nature of "the aging process" both sides will be partly right.

In interpreting comparative data on longevity, the synchronizing role of natural selection is always relevant. Two further examples will be given. The first concerns the interesting data collected by Sacher (1959) on body size, brain size, and longevity in various mammalian species. In general large mammals live longer than small ones, and, more interesting, for mammals of the same size, those with relatively larger brains tend to live longer. The latter observation is open to two kinds of interpretation. One, the physiological, is that a larger brain itself ensures longer life, perhaps by achieving more efficient homeostasis. The other is that individuals with a potentially long life are more likely to survive to old age if they can learn by experience, and hence selection for longevity and for a large brain are likely to occur in the same species; this association is particularly apparent in the evolution of our own species.

The second example concerns "molecular aging," as illustrated by changes in collagen (reviewed by Gross 1961). Although new collagen molecules can be laid down by adult animals (e.g., in wound healing or cyclically in the uterine wall), it seems that in many places, and in particular in tendons, there is little or no replacement in adults. The physical properties of tendons change continuously with age, probably due to an increase in crosslinking between molecules. There is some evidence that these changes occur more rapidly in short-lived than in long-lived species, and this has led to the suggestion (e.g., Verzar 1963) that they provide an objective measure of physiological aging.

These facts raise a difficulty in interpretation, which is best brought out by a *reduction ad absurdum*. Let us assume that: (*a*) the changes in collagen contribute to the increase in the force of mortality with age (if they do not, then by the definition used in this paper they are not an aging process at all), and (*b*) the changes occur in adults at a rate independent of the age of the individual (if the alternative were true—i.e., that changes in collagen occur only because of some peculiarity of the internal environment of old individuals—then they would be a consequence rather than a cause of senescence).

Then if these assumptions are true of mice, how does it come about that men live thirty times as long as mice? The answer has to be either that the collagen molecules of mice have a different structure, and presumably a different primary amino acid sequence, to those of man, or that the internal environment of mice is such as to accelerate the aging of collagen. But these conclusions are absurd, since they imply that natural selection has favored the evolution of a protein structure or of an internal environment which shortens the life of the individual, and it is difficult to see what the compensating advantages could be.

In fact, both assumptions may be false; in particular, there is no evidence that changes in collagen contribute to an increasing force of mortality.

THE CLASSIFICATION OF AGING CHANGES

If as I have suggested aging is multiple, it should be possible to classify the kinds of change which may be involved. The classification offered here is not the only possible one, nor is it intended to be exhaustive; my excuse for offering it is that it is the best way to emphasize the heterogeneity of the problem.

First a distinction must be drawn between processes of development and aging—between "first we ripen" and "then we rot." This is not easy, because developmental processes lead inevitably to aging ones. For example, development gives rise to a nervous system whose cells do not divide, and in mammals to teeth which are not replaced. But the following distinction can usefully be made. A developmental process is one which has evolved because it leads to an adult adapted for survival and reproduction: an aging process is one which leads to loss of adult adaptation and to death. Thus a developmental process in which the teeth are replaced once only has been favored by selection because it makes possible precise occlusion and a division of labor between the teeth; the decay and mechanical wearing away of teeth are aging processes which happen to be unavoidable consequences of the former adaptation.

A second and in practice more difficult distinction is between cellular and organismic processes. Most aging changes involve cells. But do the cells deteriorate because they are old, or because they are part of an old organism? Two examples will show how difficult it may be to answer this question. First, the death of cells in the central nervous system probably contributes to aging. But do the cells die because they are old, perhaps from mutations in their chromosomal DNA or from damage to other unrepairable organelles, or because they are part of an old organism, perhaps because of a deterioration in the vascular supply to the brain? Or again, autoimmunity, the production by competent cells of antibodies against one of the individual's own tissues, may be an important aging process. But this could be initially a cellular process, perhaps the loss by mutation of immunological tolerance by one or a group of competent cells, or it could be caused by the breaking down in an old animal of a barrier between competent and target cells.

Organismic Processes

1. Disproportionate Growth of Parts. In one form of glaucoma, closed-angle glaucoma, fluid secreted in the posterior chamber of the eye is unable to flow forward past the lens to the outflow channel anterior to the lens. Unless corrected, this leads to a rise in intraocular pressure and to blindness. A possible cause is that the lens continues to grow throughout life, and so may become too large relative to the eyeball. If this is a correct interpretation (and I am wholly incompetent to say whether it is or not) it is a clear example of aging resulting from the disproportionate growth of parts. But I do not think this is a common cause of aging. A more usual situation, illustrated by the kidney or liver, is that the size of an organ is regulated by some kind of feedback control.

2. Absence of Replacement or Repair of Essential Parts. The most obvious and important type of aging change which might be classified under this head is the deterioration of organs in which there is no cell division. But such aging is best considered as a cellular process. But there are also extra-cellular organs which are not repaired in the adult. Two examples, mammalian teeth and tendons, have been mentioned.

3. Incomplete Repair. A serious wound leaves a permanent scar; thus even in organs with a repair mechanism, repair may not be perfect. Aging may therefore result from the cumulative effects of environmental insult to organs which, although they heal, do not heal perfectly. There is little experimental evidence on this point, and most of the positive evidence of life shortening caused by environmental stress concerns ionizing radiations, and radio-mimetic chemicals known to cause chromosome breaks. Jones (1959) has reviewed the survival of men released from prisoner-of-war camps. In most cases prisoners did not show an increased mortality after release, but prisoners of the Japanese in the Pacific area showed a significantly higher mortality during the first 3 years after release, and a smaller (and statistically insignificant) increase in mortality between 4 and 6 years after release.

4. Programmed Death. Animals and plants whose life-spans are of the same order of magnitude as a year are faced by a choice at the onset of winter. They can lay down food reserves in the hope of surviving the winter to breed in the next spring, or they can convert all their available substance into eggs and then die. Although I have expressed this anthropomorphically, the "choice" is in fact settled by natural selection. In annual plants, selection has favored a kind of "programmed death" preceded by reproduction. It is significant that many such plants can survive the winter if they are prevented from seeding. Similarly, many insects produce an adult destined to reproduce and die; such adults often lack essential organs such as mouth parts.

Usually, death occurs after reproduction because there is no selection in favor of continued survival. Occasionally there is evidence of selection actually accelerating death. Blest (1963) has shown in saturniid moths that distasteful and warningly colored species may live an appreciable time after reproduction, but that their edible and cryptically colored relatives may literally fly themselves to pieces after egg-laying; anthropomorphically, why hang around long enough to teach predators, who may eat your brothers and sisters, that you are good to eat?

Programmed death is unusual in vertebrates, whose potential life-span covers several breeding seasons, but it occurs in some marine vertebrates (lampreys, salmon) which run up rivers to breed. Nevertheless programmed death does illustrate a selective process, the balancing of reproductive success in youth against long-term survival, which has operated in a less extreme form in all animals.

Cellular Processes

Natural selection acting on the differences between cells of a tissue will tend to maintain the vigor of those cells. Why then do cells deteriorate? As suggested in an earlier paper (Maynard Smith 1962), there are three possible answers to this question:

1. Nondividing Cells. Without cell division, natural selection cannot act. Therefore changes in nondividing cells are likely to be an important cause of aging. The possibility is discussed further in the last two sections of this paper.

2. Selection Favoring "Anti-social" Cell Types. In a dividing tissue, selection will favor those cell variants which multiply most rapidly, not those which function most effectively in ensuring the survival of the individual. Cell changes, which are inherited in asexual cell multiplication, are concerned in malignant disease and in auto-immunity. It is quite possible that other less dramatic changes, perhaps mutational in origin, may be involved in aging.

3. Clonal Aging. If all the cells of a tissue undergo more or less synchronous changes, selection may be unable to prevent deterioration. Clonal aging, which seems to be of this kind, has been described by Sonneborn & Schneller (1955) in paramecia in which macro-nuclear regeneration has been prevented, by Danielli & Muggleton (1959) in amoebae subsequent to prolonged starvation, and by Hayflick (1965) in cultures of human cells. In each of these cases, a period of regular and fairly rapid multiplication was followed by a slowing down of division and final loss of the clone.

Any explanation of this phenomenon must account for the fact that a large number of divisions occur before the rate slows down; for example, Hayflick found that in tissue cultures some 50 cell divisions occurred before the onset of senescence. This fact rules out two possible kinds of aging change.

First, clonal aging cannot be due to the gradual exhaustion of some irreplaceable reserve substance, or the wearing out of an irreplaceable organ; it is inconceivable that a substance be diluted by a factor of 2^{50} before senescence sets in. Whatever the organ or system it is whose deterioration is responsible for clonal aging it must be capable of replication, and this replication must be such that when the system is damaged the damage is transmitted to the daughter cells.

Second, clonal aging cannot be due to mutation of chromosomal genes, or of any other intra-cellular organ represented twice, or only a small number of times, in each cell. For if the mutation rate of such an organelle, from functional to nonfunctional, were high enough to cause aging despite natural selection favoring the nonmutant forms, then it would cause very rapid senescence, after only a few cell divisions.

One type of mechanism which could account for clonal aging is as follows. Suppose there are in each cell a large number N of equivalent organelles. These organelles can replicate, and the number per cell is constant. They can exist in two forms, functional and nonfunctional, each of which at replication gives rise to its own kind. There is a high rate of mutation from the functional to the nonfunctional form. The number of functional organelles per cell, initially N, will then decline. If it is supposed that the capacity of a cell to divide (its "fitness") declines when the number of functional organelles falls below some threshold level, then provided that N is large, results of the kind obtained by Hayflick could be explained.

The behavior of such systems is being investigated further mathematically. But the main point seems to be that a genetic mechanism consisting of the accurate copying of a complex message represented only a few times in each cell will, in a dividing tissue, confer immortality, at the expense of ultimate evolutionary change. A genetic mechanism consisting of a message represented many times in each cell, with a lower degree of accuracy of copying, ensures phenotypic constancy for a time, but can lead to clonal aging despite contrary selection.

If we suppose that clonal aging occurs by the type of process suggested, we have to explain why it does not occur in germ line cells, in protozoa in normal circumstances, or in some aneuploid and malignant cell lines. The answer must be that in these cells the organelles whose deterioration causes clonal aging can be replaced using information from the chromosomal genes. If this conclusion is correct, it has interesting implications for theories of differentiation and malignancy.

RADIATION, SOMATIC MUTATION, AND AGING

One of the most widely held theories of senescence is that it is the consequence of somatic mutation occurring in nondividing cells (e.g., Failla 1960, Szilard 1959, Curtis 1963). By somatic mutations are meant changes in the chromosomal DNA of somatic cells of a kind which, if they occurred in the germ line, would be recognized as genetic mutations. Curtis makes explicit the idea that somatic mutations are important primarily in nondividing cells, but the assumption is implicit in the theories of Failla and Szilard.

The first reason why such theories must be taken seriously is that, even if no other senescent changes occurred, animals, some of whose essential tissues consist of nondividing cells, would ultimately die from the effects of somatic mutation. The question at issue is not whether somatic mutations occur, but whether they are common enough to contribute significantly to aging.

A second reason is that ionizing radiations, in doses too small to cause acute radiation sickness, are known to shorten life. Lindop & Rotblat (1961) found that single doses of X-rays given to young mice caused a reduction in mean life-span roughly proportional to dose. Since such radiations are known to cause genetic mutations, it has been suggested that they shorten life by causing somatic mutations, and that in doing so they are mimicking the normal aging process, which is also due to somatic mutation.

There are three possible interpretations of the fact that ionizing radiations shorten life:

(a) Radiation produces more or less instantaneous changes which are physiologically similar or identical to those normally responsible for senescence in unirradiated individuals. Such an effect can be called "precocious" aging.

(b) One or more aging processes proceed more rapidly in individuals which have been irradiated than in those which have not. This can be called "accelerated" aging.

(c) Radiation sets off changes which ultimately cause death, but which do not occur in unirradiated individuals, or which proceed too slowly to contribute significantly to death.

These three possibilities are shown diagrammatically in Figure 2. Diagrams of this type have been used in discussions of aging by Strehler (1962) and others; since I find them illuminating, and shall use them below in comparing different theories, I must digress to explain the assumptions lying behind them. It is supposed that the physiological state of an individual at any time can be represented by a point in multi-dimensional space. In any given environment, this point must lie within a given region; should it pass outside this region the individual will die. For purposes of representation, the physiological state is supposed to vary in a single dimension only, and is shown as declining continuously with age, until it falls below a threshold value T, at which stage the individual dies. The weakness of this method of representation is shown by the difficulty of illustrating the third possibility listed above; thus Figure 2 is not to be taken as meaning that irradiated individuals change in the opposite manner to unirradiated ones, but only that they change in a different manner.

If either the theories of precocious or of accelerated aging are true, we would expect the causes of death in irradiated and unirradiated populations to be similar; if the third possibility is true, then irradiated individuals will die from causes—for example, malignant disease—which are rare or absent in unirradiated populations. Lindop & Rotblat (1961) have shown that in mice the causes of death in irradiated populations are similar, although not identical, to those in unirradiated ones, and that a number of causes of death, both malig-

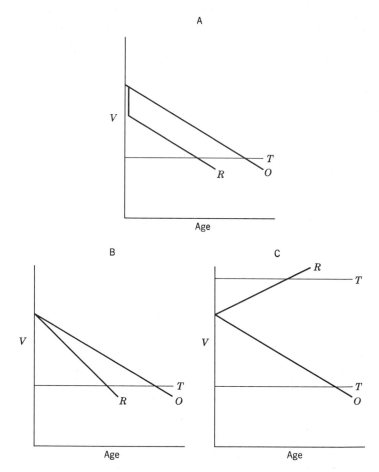

Fig. 2. Three theories of radiation-induced life shortening. The "vitality" *V* changes with age; when it falls below a threshold *T*, death occurs: *O*, unirradiated; *R*, irradiated. A, precocious aging; B, accelerated aging; C, radiation-specific aging.

nant and otherwise, act earlier in irradiated populations. But such post-mortem examinations can be difficult to interpret, partly because the cause of death can only be determined with confidence in a minority of cases, and partly because an individual which dies of one cause can provide no evidence as to whether other causes of death have also been brought forward in time by irradiation.

Alexander & Connell (1963b) have tried to get round these difficulties by serially killing and examining irradiated and unirradiated mice. They found a number of different patterns of response:

(a) Benign hepatomas did not alter either in incidence or in age of onset in the irradiated population. Earlier (1960) they had shown that another aging change, the force of contraction of collagen fibers on heating, is likewise unaffected by irradiation.

(b) Lung tumors had the same incidence in irradiated and control groups, but developed some 10 months earlier in the former. This is the pattern to be expected either from accelerated or precocious aging.

(c) Cataracts were common in the irradiated group, and were morphologically of a different type from the rare cases of cataract in the control population. In this case, therefore, irradiation has set off changes which do not occur in unirradiated mice.

If aging is multiple, there is nothing particularly surprising about this variety of response. It may be that the three possibilities illustrated in Figure 2 are all true, but of different aging processes.

We can now return to the problem of somatic mutation. The main difficulty in making a direct test of such theories lies in the difficulty of detecting the occurrence of somatic mutations in individual cells. There is one class of mutational event—structural rearrangement of chromosomes—which can fairly easily be seen. But they can be seen only at the time of cell division, and if they do occur in a dividing tissue they are likely to be eliminated by selection. Thus the frequency of chromosomal aberrations in dividing cells is a poor guide to their frequency in nondividing ones.

An ingenious way out of this difficulty has been found by Curtis (1963), who has provided the strongest evidence so far in favor of a somatic mutation theory of aging. Liver cells do not normally divide in adult mice, but can be provoked to do so if part of the liver is destroyed. By examining the cells of a liver which has recently been caused to start regenerating in this way, it is possible to estimate the frequency of chromosomal rearrangements in the nondividing liver cells immediately prior to regeneration.

Using this technique, Curtis reached the following conclusions:

(a) The frequency of chromosomal aberrations increases with age. The rate of increase was greater in a strain of mice with a low expectation of life than in a strain with a high expectation of life.

(b) X-rays cause large numbers of chromosomal aberrations.

(c) When nitrogen mustard, a powerful mutagen, was injected twice weekly in amounts approaching the lethal dose, this had no effect on longevity. At first sight this might seem to tell against a somatic mutation theory. However, Curtis points out that although nitrogen mustard causes chromosomal aberrations in the dividing cells of bone marrow, it was found not to cause chromosomal aberrations in the liver. He therefore suggests that nitrogen mustard does not cause mutations in nondividing cells, and therefore does not shorten life.

But there are a number of difficulties with this interpretation. The first concerns the effects of chemical mutagens. The fact that nitrogen mustard does not cause chromosome breaks in liver cells does not prove that it does not cause mutations in them. Therefore its failure to shorten life may merely mean that somatic mutations are irrelevant to life-shortening. This conclusion is suggested by the work of Alexander & Connell (1960, 1963a), who have compared the life-shortening effects of a bifunctional alkylating agent, myleran, and a monofunctional alkylating agent, ethyl methane sulfonate (EMS). Both these substances are known to be powerful mutagenic agents in drosophila, but the former is much more toxic than the latter, both in mice and drosophila. The probable reason for the greater toxicity of myleran is that, by causing chromosome breaks, it kills rapidly dividing cells in a few days and may kill cells not undergoing division at the time of treatment if they subsequently enter division. Alexander & Connell found that in sublethal doses myleran did shorten the life of mice, but that EMS did not. This suggests that the life-shortening effects of X-rays and some chemical mutagens arise because they break chromosomes, particularly in dividing tissues, and not because they cause point mutations.

A second reason for suspecting that X-rays may shorten the life of mice because of the effects on dividing cells lies in the discrepancy between the dose of approximately 1000 r X-rays required to reduce the life-span of a mouse to one half, and the dose of 50,000 r which halves the life of an adult drosophila. This is not because of a greater inherent resistance to radiation of insect cells, since larval insects are somewhat more sensitive to radiation than mice. The likely explanation is that, except in the gonads, there is no cell division in adult drosophila, and that irradiation shortens the life of mice primarily because of its effects on dividing cells.

A third and perhaps more serious difficulty has been pointed out by Curtis himself. It is that the number of chromosomal aberrations caused by irradiation is large compared with that in old mice. Thus a young mouse which has received a dose of fast neutrons sufficient to reduce its expectation of life by only a few months will show abnormalities in more than 50% of its liver cells, and this proportion does not decrease with time after exposure. Yet a mouse 1 year old shows abnormalities in only some 20% of liver cells. Curtis suggests that the explanation of this discrepancy may be that many gene mutations in adult cells have very delayed effects, because mRNA transcripts of the genes exist in the cytoplasm and may survive the mutation of their parent genes for many months. This raises the interesting problem of the rate of turnover of mRNA in nondividing cells. But in any case it is not clear to me that the suggestion saves the somatic mutation theory, since if messenger molecules have a life-span of the same order of magnitude as a mouse, then radiation is more likely to shorten life by destroying messenger molecules than by destroying genes.

For many reasons, it is much easier to test the theory that aging is due to somatic mutation in nondividing cells by studying insects. In adult drosophila there is no cell division outside the gonads. Hence a number of processes which may be important in the aging of mammals—for example, malignancy, autoimmunity, disproportionate growth—cannot be relevant in drosophila. We are therefore justified in hoping that we are studying a simpler system. Insects have the additional advantages that their life-spans are short enough to make experimental work tolerable, that they are poikilotherms and hence the aging process can be studied at different temperatures, and most important of all that it is possible to compare haploids, diploids, and triploids.

I will consider in turn the theories that aging is due to recessive somatic mutations, and that it is due to a combination of dominant and recessive mutations. The role of recessive mutations is most easily studied in the solitary wasp *Habrobracon,* in which females are diploid and males may be either haploid or diploid. Clark & Rubin (1961) showed that the life-spans of haploid and diploid males are the same, but that the degree of life-shortening caused by X-rays, either to the adult or pupa, is much greater in haploids. This suggests that radiation shortens life by causing recessive mutations, but that such mutations are not important in normal aging. But although there is clearly some truth in this interpretation, it is unlikely that the whole effect of X-rays arises from the induction of recessive lethals, for the following reason.

Let us assume that radiation-induced life shortening in both haploids and diploids is entirely due to recessive cell lethals. Let the number of targets per cell be N in a haploid and $2N$ in a diploid. Let r be the dose of radiation required to halve the life-span of a haploid, and R the equivalent dose for a diploid.

Let f be the fraction of cells which are not killed or rendered nonfunctional by such a dose; it is reasonable to assume that f is the same for haploids and diploids. Then for a particular gene locus in a haploid, the probability that a mutation takes place is kr, and hence the proportion of cells in which no mutation occurs,

$$f = (1 - kr)^N \to e^{-krN}.$$

Similarly in a diploid the probability that two homologous genes mutate is k^2R^2, and hence

$$f = (1 - k^2R^2)^N \to e^{-k^2R^2N};$$

hence

$$kr = k^2R^2 \text{ or } k = r/R^2$$

and hence

$$f = e^{-(r/R)2N}.$$

Now in *Habrobracon* r is approximately 10,000 rads and R is 50,000 rads. Hence

$$f \simeq e^{-N/25}$$

or

$$N \simeq -25 \ln f.$$

We do not know the value of f, the number of cells still functional after a dose of radiation sufficient to halve the life-span. But it can hardly be less than 0.5, and might well be greater than 0.9. It follows that N cannot be greater than 17, and might well be as low as 3. Now N is the number of genes (strictly, cistrons) whose products are essential if a cell in an adult is to survive and perform its function. The conclusion is clearly absurd. It follows that radiation-induced life shortening in *Habrobracon* is not wholly due to recessive somatic mutations. In fact recessive mutations are an important cause of life shortening in haploid males, but must be almost irrelevant in diploid males, and are also irrelevant to normal aging either in haploids or diploids.

In drosophila, there is even less reason to think that recessive somatic mutations are important. Lamb (1964, 1965) has shown that in *D. subobscura* the proportional reduction in life-span in males and females for a given dose of X-rays is the same, even though approximately 20% of gene loci are haploid in males and diploid in females. This effectively rules out the possibility that recessive mutation is important. (A similar argument cannot be applied to mammals, even though males and females are about equally sensitive to the life-shortening effects of radiation, because if the "Lyon hypothesis" (1961) is correct, sex-linked loci are effectively haploid in female mammals. But mutants such as *yellow* and *singed* demonstrate that the Lyon hypothesis does not apply to drosophila.)

Thus the only evidence to suggest that recessive somatic mutation is relevant to aging in insects is the fact that haploid *Habrobracon* are more radio-sensitive than diploids, and the same experiments show that recessive mutation plays little part in normal aging either in haploid or diploids.

There remains the possibility that dominant somatic mutation may be important either in normal or in radiation-induced aging. In an earlier paper (1962) I rejected this possibility on the grounds that most dominant mutations are in fact structural changes in chromosomes and become manifest only after cell division; if so they are unlikely to be relevant in nondividing cells, and in dividing cells will be eliminated by selection. This argument is less convincing now that a class of dominant point mutations which affect mechanisms controlling gene activity has been demonstrated in bacteria (Jacob & Monod 1961). It seems likely that a comparable class of mutations occurs in higher organisms, although they will be difficult to detect because of their lethality. The theory that radiation-induced life shortening is due in part to dominant and in part to recessive somatic mutations is difficult to test by comparing the sensitivities of haploids and diploids, or of males and females, because the theory has sufficient arbitrary constants to fit a wide variety of experimental results. Lamb & Maynard Smith (1964) suggested that it might be tested by comparing diploid and triploid female drosophila, since the theory predicts that the latter should be more radiosensitive. This experiment has now been done (Lamb 1965), with the results shown in Figure 3.

Although the absolute longevities of the triploids and of two classes of diploids are different, the proportional reduction in life-span for a given dose of X-rays is the same for each. Although not decisive, this is evidence against the involvement of dominant somatic mutation. It might be objected that it is not the life shortening as a fraction of the control which should be compared, but the absolute life shortening in days for a given dose; by the latter method of comparison, the triploids are in fact more sensitive. There is some internal evidence against such a procedure; if it were adopted one would have to explain why the two classes of diploids are not equally sensitive. There are also more general grounds, considered in a moment, for preferring relative to absolute values of life shortening.

The best that can be said for the view that aging, or radiation-induced life shortening, is due to dominant somatic mutations is that it is difficult to disprove. But the facts at present do little to support it.

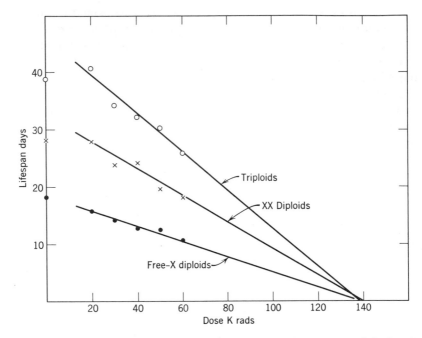

Fig. 3. Life-span after a single dose of X-rays delivered to young adult females, for triploid and two kinds of diploid *Drosophila melanogaster* (Lamb 1965). In calculating the regression lines, the life-spans of the unirradiated controls have been ignored, because small doses of irradiation prolong the life of females by sterilizing them.

A number of experiments on the effects of single doses of X-rays on the life-span of drosophila (Lamb 1964, 1965) give an astonishingly simple and consistent picture; they can be summarized as follows:

(*a*) For a given strain of flies in a given environment, life shortening is proportional to dose. (The only exception to this rule is that small doses prolong the life of females by sterilizing them; this effect is shown in Figure 3, except for the free-X diploids, which happen to be sterile in any case.)

(*b*) If the control life-span is altered by environmental means, either by changing the temperature or by altering the frequency of transfer, over a range from 15 to 105 days, the proportional reduction in life-span for a given dose is the same (Figure 4).

(*c*) The proportional reduction in life-span for a given dose is the same for males and females (Figure 4) and for diploid and triploid females (Figure 3).

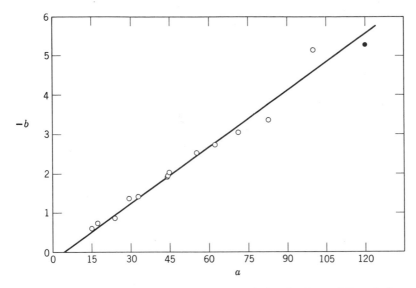

Fig. 4. Comparative radiosensitivity of male and female *Drosophila subobscura.* *a,* life-span of unirradiated flies in days; *b,* reduction in life-span in days per 4250 r. Each point represents an experiment in which flies were exposed to doses of X-rays varying from 0 to 68,000 r; in different experiments the flies were kept at different temperatures and were transferred at varying intervals to fresh food medium. Open circles, males; closed circle, ovaryless females.

(*d*) Preliminary evidence suggests that if single doses of X-rays are given to flies of different ages, a given dose produces a given proportional reduction in further expectation of life.

To some extent these results can be paralleled for mammals. In mice, life shortening is proportional to dose, males and females are equally sensitive, and doses at different ages cause equal proportional reductions in further expectation of life.

It is very difficult to see how these very simple results on insects could arise if irradiation shortens life by setting off changes which do not occur in unirradiated individuals, so that we are left with a choice between precocious and accelerated aging. But before discussing this point, it is necessary to decide why it is that flies kept in different environments have different life-spans. Two possible theories to account for this are illustrated in Figure 5; I shall call these theories the 'rate of living" theory and the "threshold" theory. The rate of living theory holds that, in different environments, aging processes proceed at different rates, death occurring when the same terminal state is reached. The experimental objections to this view have been

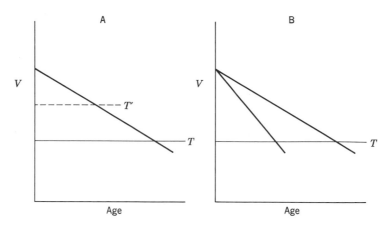

Fig. 5. Two theories to account for difference of life-span in different environments: A, the threshold theory; B, the rate of living theory.

discussed at length elsewhere (Clarke & Maynard Smith 1961; Maynard Smith 1963), and I will mention here only two difficulties.

The first concerns the longevity of flies transferred to fresh food every fourth day, compared to those transferred every 2 days; the latter live appreciably longer than the former. Flies transferred every fourth day tend to die on the last day before transfer because the food dries out, but they do so only when "middle aged"; young flies can withstand four-daily transfer quite happily. Thus if at 20° C flies are transferred every fourth day for the first month of their lives, and then every second day, they live for as long as flies which have been transferred every second day since the time of emergence. In other words, the difference in longevity in the two "environments" is not due to differences in the rate at which flies age, but to the fact that on a four-daily transfer regime they die at at earlier stage. Yet Lamb found that the proportional reduction in life-span for a given dose of X-rays was the same in the two environments.

Much more surprising, the differences in longevity of flies kept at different temperatures also seem to be largely due to a difference in the state reached before death occurs rather than to differences in the time taken to reach a given state. One experiment leading to this conclusion is shown in Figure 6.

These experiments support the "threshold" theory, according to which aging proceeds at the same (or at an only slightly changed) rate in different environments, but that in a severe environment death occurs at an earlier stage.

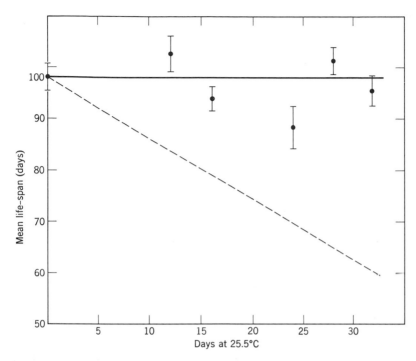

Fig. 6. Life-spans of male *Drosophila subobscura* kept for varying periods at 25.5°C and then transferred to 20°C until they died. The mean life-span of flies kept continuously at 25.5°C was 43.1 days. Full line, expectation on threshold theory; broken line, expectation on rate of living theory (Maynard Smith 1963).

Returning now to the distinction between precocious and accelerated aging, Figure 7 shows the consequences of the two theories, on the assumption that the threshold theory is correct, as it appears to be at least for the environmental differences studied in Lamb's radiation experiments. It is apparent that the precocious aging theory predicts a constant absolute life shortening for a given dose of radiation in different environments, and not a constant proportional life shortening, as is in fact observed, and as is predicted by the accelerated aging theory.

It follows that the accelerated aging theory, at first sight less plausible, fits the facts better. The difficulty lies in conceiving of a change A-A′ which could accelerate subsequent aging changes. One possible model is as follows. Suppose that in each cell there exist a large number N of target organs, which are not replaced in some or all of the cells of an adult insect. These organs can be thought of as ribosomes, but they need not be. Each organ manufactures products

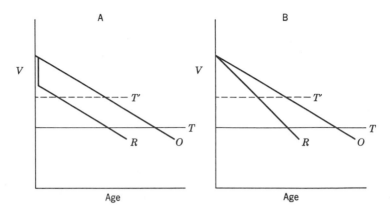

Fig. 7. Expected results of radiation on life-span in different environments, if the threshold theory is true, according to whether radiation causes A, precocious aging, or B, accelerated aging.

at a rate v and with efficiency E; if the organs are ribosomes, v is the number of protein molecules produced per unit time, and E the proportion of them which have the correct amino acid sequence.

It is then assumed that the efficiency E of any particular organ decreases with use; E is then a decreasing function of n, the number of products manufactured by that organ. This decline in E is the main aging process, and death occurs when E falls below some threshold value, which may vary with the environment in which the individual is living at the time. In the case of ribosomes, the older the individual the larger the proportion of "incorrect" protein molecules produced, and the lower the temperature the higher the proportion of incorrect molecules it can have and still survive.

The rate at which E declines will depend on v. It is reasonable to suppose that the total rate at which efficient products are made by a cell, NvE, is kept constant by some feedback mechanism. This total rate may vary in different environments. What is important is that v, and hence the rate of aging, is inversely proportional to N, the number of functional organs in a cell.

Some assumption must now be made as to the effect of irradiation. If it were supposed that irradiation caused a decline in E, this would be a "precocious aging" theory. But let us suppose that irradiation does not alter E but does destroy complete target organs, the probability that any particular organ is destroyed being proportional to dose.

If N_0 is the number of functional organs before irradiation, then after a dose R the number of functional organs is $N \simeq N_0 (1 - kR)$. And hence in any environment

$$\frac{\text{life-span of irradiated individual}}{\text{life-span of unirradiated individual}} = \frac{N}{N_0} \simeq 1 - kR$$

which agrees with observation.

To summarize this discussion of insect aging, it seems unlikely that somatic mutation is important in normal aging, although it may be partly responsible for radiation-induced life shortening in haploids. The data on the effects of radiation in different environments suggest that radiation may act by accelerating subsequent aging rather than by causing precocious aging. A simple mechanism of accelerated aging can be suggested, but the theory is perhaps too simple to be true.

PROTEIN SYNTHESIS AND AGING

In seeking for the cause of aging in nondividing cells, it is natural to look at the protein-synthetic mechanism. It is at present a hopeful hypothesis that nucleic acids are the only complicated structures with the capacity for self replication, that they influence the behavior and morphology of cells by their role in protein synthesis, and that the properties of cells are determined by the kinds of protein molecules present. If this hypothesis, or group of hypotheses, is correct, then the aging of cells must involve in the first place changes in the protein-synthetic mechanism.

But first, if these hypotheses are false, what else could be true? There seem to be four possibilities, of which only the last two are at all likely:

(a) Aging is due to changes in the relative concentrations of small molecules. This seems unlikely, except insofar as small molecules may be involved in the signaling systems determining the activities of genes, and so in aging changes of the kind referred to as "differentiation-type aging" below.

(b) Aging is due to changes in large information-carrying molecules other than nucleic acids and proteins. There is at present no reason to suspect the presence of such molecules.

(c) Aging is due to changes in supra-molecular structures whose nature is not fully specified by the nature of the protein or other molecules composing them. Sonneborn's work on paramecium (1963) suggests that such structures may be present; if they prove to be of general occurrence, changes in them may be important in aging.

(*d*) Aging is due to changes in some supra-molecular structure whose nature is determined, not by the kinds of protein molecules present or now being synthesized, but by the kinds of protein molecules present at some earlier time—for example, at the time of the previous cell division. Thus it is quite possible that some organelles are not replaced in nondividing cells, even though the cell is still capable of making their constituent molecules. This may be the case, but in practice, the process will be difficult to distinguish from the "differentiation-type" aging next to be described.

Turning now to changes in the protein-synthetic mechanism itself, two kinds of change can be distinguished at the outset:

(*1*) Differentiation-type changes, involving alterations in the relative amounts of the different protein species, but not the synthesis of proteins with changed amino-acid sequences.

It is known that differentiation involves changes in the relative activities of different genes. Aging may be a consequence of such changes. For example, a nerve cell in an adult mammal may lose the capacity to synthesize an essential enzyme, either because no mRNA for that enzyme was present in the newly differentiated nerve cell, or more plausibly because no further mRNA could be produced due to repression of the corresponding gene. Such permanent repression of the structural gene for an essential enzyme could be a normal result of development, present in all the nerve cells of a young adult, and analogous, at the organismic level, to the inability of a young adult mammal to grow new teeth; or it could arise in some or all of the cells of old individuals, due to a gradual breakdown of the complex feed-back mechanisms determining the activities of genes, analogous to the aging of an organism due to the disproportionate growth of parts.

(2) Sequence changes, involving the synthesis of proteins with abnormal aminoacid sequences.

Somatic mutation would be an aging change of this kind, but arguments for doubting its importance have been given. These arguments hinged mainly on the fact that typically two, but occasionally one or three copies of each gene are present in a cell. They are therefore not relevant to theories suggesting that aging is due to errors in protein synthesis at a later stage—for example, because of mutation-like changes in mRNA or because of faulty translation from mRNA to protein.

A particularly ingenious theory of this kind has been suggested by Orgel (1963). Suppose a single error were made in the synthesis of an activating enzyme—for example, the substitution of a serine for a leucine residue—and that in consequence the enzyme combined the wrong amino acid with the wrong transfer molecule. Since each activating enzyme activates many amino acids in its lifetime, it is conceivable that the faulty molecule might cause the synthesis of more than one similarly faulty molecule, either immediately or via the production of other types of faulty activating enzyme. If so there would be an exponential increase in the frequency of errors in protein synthesis.

The difficulty with this theory is that it is almost too successful—for example, how do germ cells escape? If the initiating events were rare, but killed cells in a time short in comparison with the lifetime of the individual, then "infected" cells would be eliminated from the germ line and other dividing tissues by selection, but could still be important in nondividing cells. But if the initiating events were relatively common and took a long time to kill cells, it is difficult to see how any of us are here at all. I see no way of estimating the frequency of initiating events; it may be that they never occur, or that genotypes which permit their occurrence have been eliminated by selection. But it might be possible for someone better versed than I in molecular biology to estimate the time from initiating event to cell death. If this time is short relative to the life-span, then such events may be important in aging; if it is long relative to the life-span, they may have been a constraint on the evolution of activating enzymes.

There is one observation which suggests that sequence changes may be important in aging in drosophila, although it is open to other interpretations. My colleague, Miss Clarke, and I have been measuring the rate of protein synthesis in adult *D. subobscura* by feeding known amounts of tritiated leucine to adult males, and measuring activity in protein 1 hr later. Measurements on males lacking testes show that synthesis in the testis (the only tissue in which cell division is going on) contributes only a small part of the total turnover. At a constant temperature of 20°C the turnover rate is such that approximately one part in 3000 of the total protein present in a fly is replaced per hour. This figure is consistent either with a large part of the protein turning over very slowly, individual molecules having a life-span of the same order of magnitude as a fly (i.e., 80 days), or with a small fraction of the protein turning over rapidly, the rest not being replaced at all. Experiments in which flies fed on labeled leucine were subsequently fed on more concentrated but unlabeled leucine, so as effectively to remove the label from the amino acid pool, have shown that once label is incorporated into protein there is no measurable decrease in activity in a further 2 days. Allowing for the inaccuracies in measurement, this shows that even those species of protein with the most rapid turnover have a mean life of at least 4 days, and perhaps much longer.

A surprising and unexpected result of these experiments is that at a given temperature the rate of incorporation of labeled leucine increases with age, being approximately twice as great at 60 days as at 7 days; measurements have shown that this difference is not due to changes in the size of the leucine pool with age. (The rate of incorporation of labeled uracil into RNA also increases with age, but we do not yet know whether this reflects an increased rate of synthesis or a reduction in the uracil pool.)

The most likely explanation is as follows. An adult fly, without cell division and at a constant temperature, can in the short term be regarded as in a steady state, with the rate of synthesis of each enzyme regulated to ensure constant enzyme activity. An increased rate of synthesis could therefore be caused either by an increased rate of protein denaturation in old flies, or by the fact that an appreciable proportion of the new protein synthesized is enzymically inactive. At present we cannot decide between these possibilities. But the results so far obtained encourage us in the idea that changes in the protein synthetic mechanism are an important aging process in drosophila.

References

Alexander, P. and Connell, D. I. (1960). *Radiat. Res., 12,* 38.

Alexander, P. and Connell, D. I. (1963a). In *Cellular Basis and Aetiology of Late Somatic Effects of Ionizing Radiation,* Harris, R. J. C., Ed., Academic Press, London, p. 259–263.

Alexander, P. and Connell, D. I. (1963b). *Ibid.,* 277–283.

Blest, A. D. (1963). *Nature, London, 197,* 1183–1186.

Clark, A. M. and Rubin, M. A. (1961). *Radiat. Res., 15,* 244–253.

Clarke, J. M. and Maynard Smith, J (1961). *J. Exp. Biol., 38,* 679–684.

Curtis, H. J. (1963). *Science, 141,* 686–694.

Danielli, J. F. and Muggleton, A. (1959). *Gerontologia, 3,* 76–90.

Failla, G. (1960). In *The Biology of Aging,* Strehler, B. L., and others, Eds., American Institute of Biological Sciences, Washington, p. 170–175.

Gross, J. (1961). In *Structural Aspects of Ageing,* Bourne, G. H., Ed., Pitman, London, p. 177–195.

Hayflick, L. (1965). *Exp. Cell Res., 37,* 614–636.

Hollingsworth, M. J. and Bowler, K. (1966). *Exp. Geront., 1,* 251–257.

Jacob, F. and Monod, J. (1961). *J. Molec. Biol., 3,* 318–356.

Jones, H. B. (1959). In *Handbook of Aging and the Individual,* Birren, J E., Ed., University of Chicago Press, Chicago, p. 336–363.

Krohn, P. L. (1962). *Proc. Roy. Soc.*, *B157*, 128–147.

Lamb, M. J. (1964). *J. Insect Physiol.*, *10*, 487–497.

Lamb, M. J. (1965). *Exp. Geront.*, *1*, 181–187.

Lamb, M. J. and Maynard Smith, J. (1964). *Exp. Geront.*, *1*, 11–20.

Lindop, P. J. and Rotblat, J. (1961). *Proc. Roy. Soc.*, *B154*, 332–349.

Lyon, M. (1961). *Nature, London, 190*, 372–373.

Maynard Smith, J. (1962). *Proc. Roy. Soc.*, *B157*, 115–127.

Maynard Smith, J. (1963). *Nature, London, 199*, 400–402.

Medawar, P. B. (1952). In *An Unsolved Problem in Biology*, Lewis, H. K., London.

Orgel, L. E. (1963). *Proc. Nat. Acad. Sci. U.S.A.*, *49*, 517–521.

Sacher, G. A. (1959). *The Lifespan of Animals*, Vol. 5 of CIBA Foundation Colloquia on Ageing, Churchill, London, p. 115–133.

Sonneborn, T. M. (1963). In *The Nature of Biological Diversity*, Allen, J. M., Ed., McGraw-Hill, New York, p. 165–221.

Sonneborn, T. M. and Schneller, M. (1955). *J. Protozool.*, *2* (suppl.), 6.

Strehler, B. L. (1962). *Time, Cells and Aging*, Academic Press, New York.

Szilard, L. (1959). *Proc. Nat. Acad. Sci. U.S.A.*, *45*, 30–45.

Verzar, F. (1963). *Scientific American, 208*, No. 4, 104–114.

Williams, G. C. (1957). *Evolution, 11*, 398–411.

DISCUSSION

DR. KOHN: You have suggested that there is a special category of programmed death for plants and some insects but in a sense, is not the life-span of animals under the same sort of control?

DR. MAYNARD SMITH: It is quite true that all death is a consequence of a developmental program. However, there is a distinction. Death in annual plants can be thought of as the consequence of natural selection favoring developmental processes which cause the plant to move all its food out of its leaves into its seeds. The same thing is true of some insects. If, however, you consider a mammal, the design of the developmental process is such that it could not possibly live forever. Nevertheless, the death in old age is an unselected and unfavored byproduct of a developmental process which has been favored by selection for other reasons.

DR. KOHN: Is not the fact that man, for example, all over the world has a life-span of something over 70 years of age today, an example of the evolution of a species specific longevity?

DR. MAYNARD SMITH: I definitely believe that the longevity of the species is a variable under genetic control as is height, or the number of eggs laid, or the color of the eyes. I do not believe that natural selection has favored death, except in special cases where there is the programmed death that I have just described. I do not think that selection is acting on mice to make sure that they die in 2 years in order to make room for their juniors. This is an argument developed by Weissmann but I believe it is nonsense!

DR. KOHN: Cells in the central nervous system can live longer than 70, 80, or so years, cells of the GI tract or granulocytes of the white cell series have a life-span of maybe a few days. They are all post-mitotic cells but while the cells of granulocytic series seem to die out with a programmed senescence, at a rate of dying which is proportional to the length of time they have lived, the cells of the central nervous system seem to drop out at random.

The fact that we can predict life expectancy means that there is a program there. The argument is about where the program is, in the DNA or elsewhere. You want to define programming as a developmental process depending on genetic information. I think it is a limited use of the word program.

DR. MAYNARD SMITH: I would want to use program in that sense. I think the distinction between what I have called "programmed death" and other aging processes is that in the former case there is quite a recognizable developmental process which we could see, without bothering to think about it at all, is going to lead rapidly to death.

DR. KOHN: That could be the continuation of a developmental program which has been selected upon say, through the period of growth and maturation and which, just because there is no mechanism to protect against it, keeps on for the next 30 or 40 years and finally kills.

DR. MAYNARD SMITH: I think this kind of thing happens. I would not classify it as programmed death.

DR. GLASER: How accurately can you measure the shortening of life due to irradiation?

DR. MAYNARD SMITH: Anybody who claims to demonstrate a 5% difference in the life-span of any species is a bit of optimistic; it ought to be possible to show a 10% difference.

DR. ROCKSTEIN: What about radiation induced prolongation of life?

DR. MAYNARD SMITH: You can greatly extend the life-span of a female fruitfly by irradiating her with 5–10,000 rad. The reason is that you destroy the gonads, and anything which stops a female drosophila from laying eggs makes her live longer. This can be done in several ways. A temperature shock will cause the female to live longer for the same reason. The crucial fact, however, is that the life-span of a genetically ovary-less female cannot be prolonged by radiation. Dr. Sacher *(Psysiological Zoology,* 1963, *36,* 295–311) and I have disagreed as to whether one can prolong the life of males by radiation. Dr. Sacher can, and I cannot.

DR. ROCKSTEIN: We can increase the life-span of male flies by one-third to one-fifth and we think that this is a genetic effect. (Rockstein, M., Dauer, M. and Bhatnagar, P. L., 1965. *J. Geront., 20,* 219–223. Also, Rockstein, M., Bhatnagar, P. L. and Dauer, M. 1965. *Exp. Geront., 1,* 149–159.) Sterile female houseflies produced either by diet or irradiation have shorter lives.

DR. MAYNARD SMITH: I do not see why you want this to be a genetic effect. I think it is a physiological effect via the gonads. I accept that there are differences between houseflies and drosophila. I am not arguing with you, but with Sacher here. Perhaps if the environment contains pathogens that are killed by radiation you may prolong the lives of animals.

DR. ROCKSTEIN: Do you have survival curves for large populations which would show a shifting, as it were, of the normal survival curve to the left? Would they not help to distinguish between precocious and accelerated aging?

DR. MAYNARD SMITH: A shift of this sort is roughly what occurs but I do not regard it as particularly valuable evidence. You cannot tell anything about the rate at which processes are going on in the individuals from the shape of life table curves and I am convinced that it is a fallacy to believe that you can. The life table tells you nothing that is going on in an individual (other than that aging processes are occurring), but something about the differences between individuals in a population. It probably tells you more about the variation of the environment than anything else.

DR. KOHN: That is precocious aging you have plotted, is it not, not accelerated aging?

DR. MAYNARD SMITH: Neither, you cannot tell from that graph which it is.

DR. KOHN: If it is accelerated aging, then the slope should increase in the irradiated area.

DR. MAYNARD SMITH: No, no, no! This is the fallacy. You can tell nothing about the rate of progress in each individual. When you are talking about precocious versus accelerated aging you are talking about how fast the processes are going on in any individual. When you look at a life table you are talking about what are the causes of the differences between the members of the population. If you did your life tables perfectly, that is to say, the members were absolutely identical in their genotype and in their environment, then, regardless of the circumstances, the life table would look rectangular. All die at the same instant. Alternatively, if all did not die at the same instant, it would show that random events are important in aging. In this case, the shape of the life table would tell you something about the differences in the incidence of random events between individuals, but nothing about the time course of events in single individuals. The shapes of life tables have misled more people into phoney speculation than any other one observation in aging.

If you have different mean expectations of life between two populations, one of which has been starved and the other has not, you can certainly tell a great deal from this difference between the life tables. What I am saying is you cannot tell a lot from the shape of the individual life table; it is like trying to deduce the rate of growth of a child from the distribution of heights in an adult population. Comparing different life tables is a most fruitful way of studying aging—with different genotypes or different treatments— but one cannot get much information from the shape of one life table as this depends on the conditions of the experiment and the genetic variability of the population.

DR. CURTIS: Would it not help to put the radiation in at different times during the life-span of the animal?

DR. MAYNARD SMITH: Yes. Marion Lamb is actually at the moment doing these experiments. Her tentative answer is that the proportional effect is still true. A given dose of 50,000 r halves the further expectation of life regardless of the age at the time of irradiation. Lindop (*Scientific Basis of Medicine Annual Review*, 1965, p. 99) says that a given dose of radiation to mice produces a proportional reduction too and not an absolute reduction in expectation of life; that is, this is accelerated not precocious aging. Mice are much too complicated in my view. One suspects that most of radiation effects on mice are acting on dividing cells. In fruit flies, however, the action is on nondividing cells and one would not, therefore, expect the same phenomena. We ought to look at whether this is true for irradiation of pupae where there are dividing cells.

DR. KOHN: One of the very conspicuous and consistent changes after X-irradiation is not what would be interpreted as mutation but as a fibrosis around the capillaries. The process seems to be quite general and may or may not be due to death of endothelial cells. But it is a pericapillary fibrosis which is quite different from everything you have been talking about in insects or in mice.

DR. MAYNARD SMITH: My whole concept is that aging may well have multiple causes and the fact that one isolates in a species like drosophila or its equivalent, the housefly, or paramecium, a particular process, say changes in the post-mitotic cells, that looks important does not mean that it will be important in man, although it might. I think this is a difficulty of our whole subject.

DR. MEDAWAR: There are two general points which should be made at this stage. The first is the very obvious point that some aging changes do not show up in the form of increasing vulnerability. That is to say, they do not show up as an increase in the force of mortality. The example I might choose for this is the menopause in human females. This period is not marked by any kink in the life table which would suggest an increase in the force of mortality. On the contrary, it should be marked by a decrease in the force of mortality, because it marks the end of the reproductive period and therefore the removal of possible hazards associated with it.

The definition and measurement of aging is a very tricky business. The definition we all really go by is in fact a "personal" definition. We are interested in what happens in the life history of an individual organism, and we know that aging is some kind of deterioration of performance in the individual. This is not good enough as a definition because it does not lend itself to measurement. It is the great advantage of the actuarial approach that it attempts to measure the aging process by what is, in effect, merely an age-frequency distribution of the moment of death. The aging processes in two different populations can be compared by this means.

We all take it absolutely for granted that the aging process is an epiphenomenal one. That is to say, it is something superimposed upon the ordinary biological business of evolution or development. We know that a continuous series of cell division lineages, exactly equal in number to the total number of living organisms on the face of the world at this moment, has existed since the beginning of biological time. Therefore, a process of deterioration is not implicit in or automatically entailed by biological functioning. All these lineages—as I say, one for every organism alive today—have persisted since the beginning of biological time, because imperfections have been eliminated. In a sense, all aging is due to a failure to eliminate imperfection. It does not matter what the imperfections are; anything which causes the progressive deterioration in time of the performance of an individual will count. This in turn implies, as has already been mentioned, that there are various causes of aging. No one master reaction is the ultimate cause of aging.

DR. KOHN: I would suggest that one should take into account the universality of aging. This is a normal process, normal by definition because it occurs in all members of the population that we are talking about, whether it is a population of macromolecules in solution, or cells in tissue culture, or of cells within an organ, or a population of intact human beings.

DR. MAYNARD SMITH: I do have one philosophical worry about that definition. It is perhaps defeatist to use a definition which implies in principle that aging is incurable. It probably is, but it is a pity to commit ourselves to that view.

DR. KOHN: To say it is occurring now does not mean that it must always occur.

DR. BOURNE: I am not happy about the use of the terms aging and senescence. Aging means simply getting older, it does not necessarily imply senescence. The senescence process is fundamentally an intrinsic process which can be affected by certain extrinsic processes. Radiation clearly affects the length of life. Is it really doing this by affecting the process of senescence, or by some other process which interferes with the mechanics of living? Kohn's trenchant example that radiation led to a fibrosis around the capillaries and affected their mechanical functioning is a good one.

DR. MAYNARD SMITH: What I would prefer to do is to refer to things, for example, like the cataracts which occur only in irradiated animals, and do not, on the whole, occur in the unirradiated as "radiation-specific aging," thereby indicating that this is an aging process in an irradiated animal only. Naturally, in radiated animals it is, by my definition, an aging process because it leads to an increase in the force of mortality.

DR. BOURNE: But you also get cataracts from other causes, other extrinsic causes, for example, vitamin deficiency, and you cannot call that true aging.

DR. MAYNARD SMITH: Would you say that the way we wear teeth cannot be aging? It is not intrinsic, it is because we keep on eating. I really insist that the mechanical way we wear teeth is an aging process. It is a normal aging process.

DR. BOURNE: It is the consequence of an extrinsic factor. Things have become so complex that teeth reach a situation where they cannot rectify the insults that they get from extrinsic factors and therefore they gradually deteriorate.

DR. MEDAWAR: The point which is being made is that if the teeth are not used, they do not undergo this aging process whereas there are other aging processes which occur irrespective of use.

DR. GROSS: Could we start with a general proposition and then make it more specific? Namely, this is a time-dependent change which leads to loss of function, of which death is purely a symptom. If you wanted to look at time-dependent changes that lead to alterations in function go back to the simplest possible systems, where you know that the environment acts in a slow steady way to cause change, for example, the increasing insolubility that occurs in a solution of aluminum hydroxide on standing. This is a very elementary example of things which happen to molecules over a period of time. Perhaps one of the best ways to define the process is to get that simple minded, and to look at some of these very elementary changes that take place in systems of biological macromolecules and lead to loss of function because they remove functional elements from the system or add things which should not be there. These are time-dependent processes which take place in the normal course of events because of the low levels of energy in the environment that macromolecules are subject to continuously.

It is not valid to counter this argument by claiming that biomolecules do not age because they are rapidly "turning over." Many of them are not rapidly turned over and in any case, if they were, only the *rate* of loss would be affected.

DR. MAYNARD SMITH: It is important to hang on, in addition, to the concept of function, because otherwise any change including growth is aging.

DR. GROBSTEIN: Aging can be used in the sense of time-dependent change with respect to life history. In this sense, aging begins at time zero in the life history and progresses to death. So defined, growth or anything else that we call development is part of the aging process. There are obvious objections to using the word in this sense in the context of our discussion here. For example, aging also carries the connotation of senescence. It seems to me we do have to decide how to distinguish these two connotations. We must recognize that we do talk about two different phenomena when we talk about aging per se—time-dependent change—and senescence—which we define in terms of resistance to death. In attempting to use death rates to define aging, one looks at the terminal stage of the process and hence knows nothing about the events that lead to it, and certainly does not measure them. The measurements of aging for this purpose should be of the converse of death rate, that is, resistance to death. There are many parameters of death resistance and one would have to measure the resistance to death with respect to each particular characteristic that is entering into the total process. Hence, there will be different estimates of the resistance to death, depending on what stress to the organism is under observation. It is the envelope of all of these that we refer to as the general phenomenon of senescence.

DR. MAYNARD SMITH: I do not disagree in any way with what you said.

DR. ATWOOD: We have heard some speculation that clonal aging could be caused by differential replication rates of cell particulates, or irregularities of their distribution in dividing cells. I want to point out that ribosomes do not meet the requirements of such conjectures because their RNA is copied from DNA so that they do not have their own genetic continuity. But the ribosomes might have some role in aging of those fixed post-mitotic cells in which continued activity of the genetic translation system is required.

We have been working on hybridization of different kinds of RNA in drosophila with drosophila DNA and you may have seen the paper of Ritossa and Spiegelman showing that the location of the templates for ribosomal RNA in drosophila is the nucleolus organizer region on the X and Y chromosomes. A marker called *bobbed* is in that region and we guessed that this might be a deletion of part of the complex that specifies ribosomal RNA. Measurements showed, for *bobbed* stocks, that the proportion of DNA hybridizable to ribosomal RNA is much less than for normal stocks. The redundancy of the ribosomal region is of the order of 200; that is, in a normal drosophila genome there are about 200 stretches of DNA for 18S and 200 for 28S ribosomal RNA. In bobbed stocks around 50 stretches are present, depending on the allele. Alleles with the most extreme phenotypic expression have the least redundancy. We think that this redundancy is a linear array rather than a multistranded array. The probable reason for it is that, sometime in the life cycle, ribosomal RNA has to be made at a peak rate for which the rate of transcription of a single template is not sufficient. And so, these templates are transcribed concurrently to satisfy that requirement. Some functional differentiation in the region is possible, but the *bobbed* deletions are proof that functional differentiation does not account for all the multiplicity of templates. The phenotype of these flies is at least consistent with a general decrease in the rate of genetic translation. Development is delayed, the bristles are small, and sometimes the abdominal tergites are etched. Since the bristle size reflects the synthetic activity of a bristle-forming cell during a very short interval in development, it may be regarded as a sensitive indicator of protein synthesizing capacity; provided, of course, that we are not dealing with mutations specifically affecting integumentary structures. The delayed development, and the genetic basis now established for *bobbed,* indicate that its effect is indeed general. The longevity of *bobbed* flies has not yet been studied.

What might this have to do with aging? In normal mitosis the array of templates should usually be distributed equally to daughter cells, and so provide no basis for clonal aging such as might be imagined for a system of separate replicating entities. On the other hand, suppose that mutations occur in it. I imagine that some bad ribosomes may be more harmful than a mere scarcity of ribosomes. A bad one may block a polyribosomal complex and tie up those that are already there, whereas a simple depletion of ribosomes only slows down the process without interfering in a permanent way. So one could surmise that mutations in large manifold genes of this sort could be quite harmful in post-mitotic populations where cells with defective translation systems are not replaced. As for the soluble RNA, if we assume there are 60 kinds, then the redundancy for each kind in drosophila is, by similar experimental criteria, at least 15 and the foregoing remarks may pertain to soluble RNA as well as ribosomal.

One problem is, how are redundant regions prevented from becoming heterogeneous by mutation with the passage of many generations? First, mutations that are subject to immediate selection will behave as they do in non-redundant loci. Second, the length of a redundant region may be adjusted by unequal crossing over followed by selection. In our experience *bobbed* is the most unstable of markers. We surmise that the tandem stretches often pair unequally at meiosis. A consequence of crossing over in the region is that the templates are distributed unequally in the complementary crossover products. If this happens frequently, we should be able to find *bobbed* alleles in wild-type populations and less extreme alleles in *bobbed* populations, and indeed both are found with high frequency. Selection for regions of optimal length may hasten the fixation or elimination of selectively neutral mutations in the region, and thus decrease heterogeneity.

DR. BIRREN: Dr. Maynard Smith's closing remarks about protein synthesis were getting at a mechanism which most of us would agree is intrinsic. Perhaps Dr. Wulff could come in here.

DR. WULFF: The finding of increased incorporation of leucine into proteins of old adult *Drosophila subobscura* relative to younger adults is of considerable interest to me because we have obtained similar results using young and old adult rats. The specific activity of liver proteins of old rats (815–817 days) is approximately 70% higher than the specific activity of liver protein of young rats (116–118 days) both at 15 and 30 min. after intraperitoneal injection of C^{14}-leucine (Wulff, V. J., Samis, H. V., Jr. and Falzone, J. A., 1966. *Advances in Gerontological Research,* Vol. 2, B. S. Strehler, Ed., Academic Press, New York). Results obtained by Dr. Kenneth Perry on protein of rat kidney cortex and ventricular muscle show even greater age-related differences, the specific activity of "old" protein being three to ten times greater than that of "young" protein. Although these are but preliminary results, they raise the interesting possibility that, in this particular respect, the passage of time may have the same consequence in *Drosophila subobscura* and in our albino rats.

DR. KOHN: Could this be a permeability difference?

DR. WULFF: This is entirely possible. We have also injected tritiated cytidine and tritiated orotic acid intraperitoneally into young and old rats (122 days and 825 days old). The figures we have obtained for the specific activity of liver nuclear RNA suggest that there is an increased turnover in the old animals (Samis, H. V., Jr., Wulff, V. J. and Falzone, J. A., 1964. *Biochim. Biophys. Acta, 91,* 223–232). Similar results have been obtained using diced liver cultured *in vitro*.

DR. KOHN: I would question the use of liver as a model for the study of aging in the whole animal because the liver has a fantastic power of regeneration and is probably the one organ in the body in which it is very difficult to find any age related decrease in function. I have always wondered why so many people choose to work on liver rather than some other organ which is known to fail with age or which shows important age changes.

DR. WULFF: We chose the liver because it is relatively homogenous and large enough for us to use these techniques and still be relatively quantitative. Although the liver certainly has this capacity for reconstituting itself, I would argue the point that it does not age, because our findings indicate just one of the ways in which it does so.

DR. GROSS: There is a problem in looking at the specific activity alone because the protein pools are heterogeneous in composition and probably in turnover rate. For example, if in the older animal the old cold proteins are selectively removed the specific activity is going to go up; this does not mean that the incorporation rate has increased.

DR. SINEX: The other problem is the cell population present and what it is doing. For example, does an old internal elastic intima really consist of old elastin or is one entering a new stage where more elastin is being made as part of a repair process? You may be measuring in the senescent kidney or liver a response to aging injury which involves fibroblasts and proliferation of extracellular elements which are not particularly active in a normal mature healthy organ system.

DR. WULFF: Working with the intact organism creates many problems. Future work should be directed towards the measurement of protein synthesis in *in vitro* systems, preferably perhaps cell free systems. Some of our work, not in connection with protein metabolism, but with RNA metabolism, has shown that changes that exist in the intact animal do carry over to these *in vitro* systems.

DR. SINEX: Are there any differences in the metabolic activities of young and old flies.

DR. MAYNARD SMITH: A colleague of mine has been measuring the oxygen consumption of flies and finds that it is higher in the old animals.

DR. DULBECCO: Do the bacteria in the flies make any important contribution to the protein turnover?

DR. MAYNARD SMITH: I am making arrangements with Dr. Sang for the sterile culture of drosophila on defined media and propose to repeat these experiments on such sterile flies, and I also intend to study the incorporation of thymidine into DNA.

SUMMARY OF "AGING OF MICROORGANISMS"

D. A. Glaser

Department of Molecular Biology,
University of California, Berkeley,
Berkeley, California

The purpose of Dr. Glaser's contribution was to describe some of the events in the life cycle of bacteria which might provide ideas about what to look for in the life cycle of cells in higher organisms. Dr. Glaser went on to consider how the properties of bacteria could be related to his criterion of aging that it is "a loss of adaptability and function with age that increases vulnerability to lethal events." First, individual bacteria growing in an unchanging environment change with time in a number of different ways. Second, when placed in a finite volume of medium the whole culture goes through a life cycle, as a clone of cells, which might be considered to be an analogue of a higher organism. Third, bacteria can be exposed to sudden environmental disturbances such as changes of temperature or X-irradiation.

Dr. Glaser continued by discussing changes in the rates of synthesis of DNA and RNA in bacterial cultures, the expression of genes at different times in the life cycle, and pointed out that the assumption that physiology of bacteria during the stationary phase of culture is the same as that of cells in the growth phase is unfounded. If the amount of glucose available to a culture is reduced the bacteria grow more and more slowly until a level is reached at which they manage just to stay live without growing or dividing. Membrane pumps are maintained, repair enzymes continue to function, lysis is prevented, and the cells can recover their growth potential if a fresh source of energy is provided. With still less available glucose this ability to recover is lost.

Finally Dr. Glaser developed the concept of a "viability volume" describing the collective ranges of critical parameters within which continued life of the bacteria is possible. Alterations, whether caused by mutations or random fluctuations in a variety of critical concentrations, will affect the activity of enzymes, and if the boundary of the volume is overstepped the cell slows down or may die. Aging could be described as a loss of versatility or as a shrinking of the range of parameters over which a cell is viable.

DISCUSSION

DR. MAYNARD SMITH: Is there any evidence that, if you make life difficult for bacterial cultures, for example, by putting them up in an ionically difficult solution, the 3% minimal requirement for glucose goes up?

DR. GLASER: I do not know.

DR. MEDAWAR: If there is to be any analogy between the processes you are describing and aging in higher organisms you must reckon with the fact that, in spite of all the hazards that bacteria have to put up with, some do survive. But you are interested in the ones that die, not in the ones that survive. In a sense you are acting as an obituarist. It is the survivors which make the comparison with higher organisms so far fetched, because the higher organisms have no alternative but to age and die.

DR. GLASER: It follows from the definition that aging results in an increased vulnerability to death. Death itself is not the only measure of this. The range of circumstances which the cell can withstand is another. As you get older you have to be more careful with many of the things you do, you have to restrict your diet, you get pneumonia more easily, and so on. An organism can be maintained alive by coddling it. I would say that aging had occurred to get it into that predicament.

DR. MEDAWAR: However, in the higher organism there is no environment, however much you coddle it, which will keep it alive, while here—in principle—there is such an environment.

DR. PUCK: There would seem to be something fundamentally different about the aging of a metazoan and whatever a bacterium does when it stops growing. If a bacterium ceases multiplication because of a lethal mutation, this is a random event in isolated cells. If the mutation probability is small within the division time of the cell, then it cannot be the kind of aging process referred to in the former case. While one can point to many situations which on the face of them make a single cell culture look as though it is aging, it really seems that the aging phenomenon of animals is something unique, something that is not shown by micro-organisms.

DR. GLASER: I do not know very much about higher organisms, but if you needle me, I will give you the following answer. I could have plotted a hormone level in a higher organism. As the number of secretory cells capable of making that hormone decreases then the total concentration of that hormone will go down and the ability of the whole organism to face emergencies will be reduced.

DR. MAYNARD SMITH: I have a lot of sympathy with the way this is being put. I do know that nothing would keep very old drosophila alive if they are kept at 20°C. They will die the next day, come what may. At 10°C, however, they will still be alive a month later.

DR. KOHN: But as long as we do not know what to put on those dimensions, whether it is hormones or connective tissue or loss of cells, it is simply a restatement of what we already know, that with increasing age there is a higher probability of dying.

DR. GLASER: There are the built-in assertions that these variables are not unrelated and that, if you are within the favorable range of one variable, you can tolerate a wider range in another variable. If the capacity in one variable is lost, you would have to be very careful about maintaining others.

DR. KOHN: You have talked in terms of mutations, but of course this could be any change with time.

DR. GLASER: Certainly, there could be physiological flip-flops which change the state of the plasma, for instance, in a dramatic sort of way, without changing the genetic information at all. All developmental processes operate in such a way.

DR. PUCK: But the problem still remains, namely, that for these microorganisms you can always define a range of environmental parameters which as long as they are maintained, will permit reproduction to go on forever, whereas for the higher organisms there is no such definition possible. No matter how you change the environment in any way that anyone can conceive of, the animal appears to age and die.

DR. ORGEL: You can certainly say that there is no possible comparison between the death of an individual and the death of a bacterial culture which divides by binary fission. But it does seem reasonable to ask under what conditions the number of survivors is very much less than is predicted on the basis of exponential growth.

What I have in mind is that you take a bacterium, and when it divides you take the two daughters, put them in different dishes. When those divide you put the daughters in four different dishes and so on. At the end of N generation times you would find that the number of survivors is very much less than 2^N if N is large enough.

DR. PUCK: You can always find conditions where this does not hold.

DR. ORGEL: In the best conditions so far realized, bacteria die at the rate of about 10^{-4}/division. So after 10^6 divisions only 1% of the potential survivors would actually be alive.

DR. KOHN: The important question is the probability of dying related to time. If Dr. Orgel's cells in separate dishes have just as great a probability of dying the moment they are put in the dish as they do after they have been sitting in the dish for 5 months, I believe that would not be aging. If, on the other hand, the longer they sit there the greater the likelihood of dying, this would be more of an aging phenomenon.

DR. GLASER: I used bacteria to provide examples of mechanisms that might lead to the death or increased vulnerability of cells. I do not claim that bacteria age, because they go on by binary fission, and in a sense the whole culture keeps going forever, if an environment is maintained constantly. From those mechanisms, however, I can see that the survival of an organism that requires the proper functioning of the whole colony, which would then grow into a higher organism, could be described in the same way that I can describe the survival of an individual bacterium.

DR. PUCK: It might or it might not, depending on what the individual probabilities are. If the organism consists of tissues, each of which has a billion cells and these cells can reproduce and replace each other, then the probabilities have to be of a very different order and actually it may be difficult to account for aging by this kind of phenomenon.

DR. GLASER: I agree, the description is still completely unquantitative and to say whether it makes any sense requires putting numbers on it. The way to go about it is to adopt the engineer's approach when he calculates the mean time to failure of an orbiting satellite or a computer. He calculates the mean time to failure of each component. Some die like radioactive decay, a random process. Other components, like dry cells, have a finite lifetime. A transistor deteriorates in a random fashion unless it is a power transistor which gets hot and then dies in some way like a battery. To calculate the mean time to failure of a whole complicated system, the death properties of the separate pieces must first be known. Then the weak link can be identified and improved. The medical problem of aging is analogous. Try to find out what are the limiting things and which ones are of random incidence, like getting hit over the head by a falling rock, and which ones are things wearing out, and then see whether one can discover how the wearing out process works. We know what it means in the case of a rotating bearing; metal is shaved away, the dimensions change. In the case of a cell, we do not know. But the atoms are all changed within some time and, since atoms do not wear out, so it must be that the structure does not repair itself faithfully. Inaccurate repair is a thing we might call wearing out and that is what we have to study.

DR. WILLIAMS: A quantitative approach to viability or aging would be by challenging the system with some stress, say temperature, and seeing whether the animal dies.

DR. KOHN: There have been a lot of experiments such as placing mice in cold water to see how long they swim before they die. As they get older they die sooner. We know that an old individual cannot tolerate pneumonia the way a young individual can. The amount of damage in an old individual which is enough to kill him would be disregarded by a young individual.

DR. SALLMAN: I would like to describe a bacterial model for the study of cellular aging which we have utilized for the past few years, and which appears ideally suited for the investigation of metabolic changes associated with aging. We felt that such a study should be conducted under environmental conditions which would allow the cellular biosynthetic activities of growth to proceed at their maximum rate but in the absence of cell multiplication. Our system for the accomplishment of this goal consists of a thymine-requiring mutant of *Escherichia coli* 15 which is synchronously grown in a chemically defined medium, harvested, washed, and resuspended in the same growth medium minus thymine. Omission of the required pyrimidine prevented DNA synthesis and, consequently cell division; growth, however, as measured by increased cell size, respiration rates, RNA, protein and specific enzyme (beta-galactosidase) synthesis, continued unabated. The size of an ordinary *E. coli* is about $1\frac{1}{2}$ μ. These individual cells vary considerably but some will grow to 6, 8 μ or larger.

The bacterial system in which the ability to produce DNA is interfered with without affecting normal maintenance processes presents certain advantages for the study of aging at the cellular level not obtainable with tissue cells derived from plants or animals. These advantages are, for example, (*1*) the ease of obtaining unlimited numbers of cells approximately the same age by the use of synchronous cultures, (*2*) very high metabolic rates compared to those of most tissue cells, and (*3*) elimination of extracellular factors governing interdependence between cells in tissues.

Growth of the system slows down after about 6 hours and eventually the cells die but we have not yet studied this area in detail.

BIOLOGY OF AGING IN INSECTS

Morris Rockstein

Professor of Physiology,
University of Miami,
School of Medicine,
Coral Gables, Florida

Aging can be defined as that universal attribute of all multi-cellular organisms, which is characterized by time-dependent, reproducible alterations in structure and function, which may or may not be peculiar to each species or strain. *Senescence,* more specifically, is that part of the total aging process which occurs during the last trimester of adult existence and during which time-related structural and functional changes of a *degradative* nature predominate in certain organs and tissues, such as to lead ultimately to the diminished capacity of the individual to survive the assaults of both the internal and external surrounding environment.

As highly complex multicellular organisms, insects possess a number of properties particularly advantageous in the study of aging (Rockstein 1959a, 1960; Clark & Rockstein 1964).

These include:

1. Their wide diversity of habits, from free-living to parasitic, from tropical to arctic, and from aquatic to cryptic to aerial form.

2. Their large numbers, due to their high fecundity.

3. Their availability in highly-inbred to homogeneous to genetically pure strains.

4. Their small, but still experimentally manipulative size, which permits their breeding and maintenance at a relatively modest cost and with much smaller space requirements than those of larger, vertebrate animals.

5. Their short life-span—a number of strains of various species of flies and the worker honey bee, *Apis mellifera,* possess *maximum life-spans* of about 2 months and mean longevities of about half of that period of time.

Considering *senescence* specifically, aside from the most obvious external manifestation of old age (namely, the senile skin), the most commonly recognizable and universal sign of senescence is the gradually increasing failure in motor ability with advancing age, both in lower organisms as well as in man. Flight, the ability to locomote in the aerial atmosphere, represents that singular characteristic of insects which distinguishes them form other arthropods. This ability is especially well developed in the most highly evolved orders, the Diptera and Hymenoptera, which include the strongest flying insects known. However, the development of flight ability in insects is an ancient characteristic, since, according to the best records, the first winged insects existed some 250 million years ago during the upper Carboniferous period; these are represented today in the fossil Palaeodictyoptera, which resemble mayflies of somewhat medium size in comparison with contemporary insects. Since these insects are of the most generalized character, flying insects as a whole, even the highest orders, must have developed from this ancestral stock. The appearance of the higher orders of insects with complete metamorphosis (most of which are typically alate in the adult stages), on the other hand, probably occurred in the early Permian Period (215 million years ago) in the form of the Neuroptera (lacewings).

The complexity of insect flight, accomplished through the contraction of muscles moving the wings indirectly through alternate compression and elastic relaxation of the solid cuticular thoracic mass, is reflected in the unusual intimate anatomy of insect flight muscle. Such muscle typically possesses fibrils of unusual size and so has been termed by Wigglesworth (1950) "fibrillar muscle." It is made up of: (1) relatively enormous, cross-striated, longitudinal columns of fibrils in a (2) mass of sarcoplasm, and (3) in distinct zones of sarcoplasm separating adjacent fibrils, the sarcosomes or giant mitochondria. As shown in Figure 1, these mitochondria are arranged in linear fashion and have been amply demonstrated by Williams and his colleagues to be identical with the mitochondria of vertebrate tissues as regards their cytological, cytochemical, and biochemical features (Williams & Williams 1943; Watanabe & Williams 1951, 1953; Levenbook & Williams 1956). Sacktor (1953a, 1953b, 1954, 1961) particularly has demonstrated the similitude between the biochemical properties of the giant mitochondria in insectan flight muscle and those of vertebrate liver and heart muscle.

Specifically, the localization of function in relation to the above-delineated structural trichotomy of insect flight muscle has been possible from various experimental biochemical studies as follows:

1. The contractile mechanism, located in the actomyosin of the fibrils.

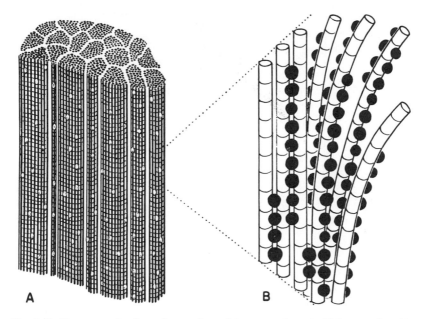

Fig. 1. A diagrammatic view of a section of insectan thoracic flight muscle. Giant mitochondria are shown as spheres in both Figures 1A (a mass of 20 fibers) and 1B (enlarged view of a single fiber) (from Williams & Williams 1943).

2. The anaerobic pathway of carbohydrate breakdown and the aerobic-pentose cycle, both located in the sarcoplasm.

3. The enzymes of the citric acid cycle, the dehydrogenases, cytochrome *c* oxidase and reductase, and the riboflavins, all of which are located in the mitochondria.

During our studies, we have established the following facts about aging in the common housefly:

1. Males have a shorter mean and maximum life-span than do females (17.4 vs. 29.4 days and 54 vs. 63 days, respectively) under conditions of constant temperature, humidity, and light, and reared and maintained on a standard diet (Figure 2; Rockstein 1957; Rockstein & Lieberman 1959).

2. Correspondingly, the wings of young male house flies begin to show signs of abrading by the middle to end of the first week, complete loss of wings in a few male flies by the end of the first week of adult life, and in practically all male flies by the onset of the third week. Females, on the other hand, show practically no loss of wings throughout this entire period, and just begin to show wing loss by

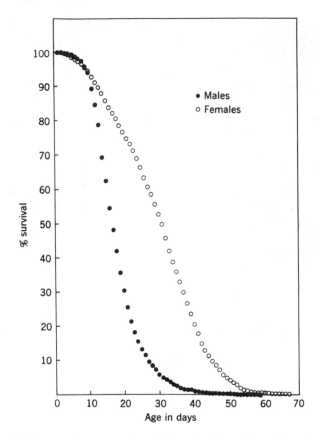

Fig. 2. Survival curves for approximately 4000 male and 4000 female houseflies, *Musca domestica* (from Rockstein & Lieberman 1959).

the middle of the third week of adult life (Figure 3; Rockstein & Brandt 1963).

Figure 4A shows a female housefly fully emerged only 5 minutes earlier, with the wings still unexpanded. Figure 4B shows a female housefly 30 min old, with the wings completely expanded and Figure 4C a female 4 days old with the wings completely intact and Figure 4D a female 18 days old with the wings intact, showing only some slight fraying or abrading in the posterior margin of the distal region of the wings. In Figure 5A, one sees a male housefly 30 min old with the wings completely expanded and the animal ostensibly able to fly fully. Figure 5B shows a 4 day-old male housefly with its posterior portions of wings showing fairly pronounced signs of fraying or abrading and Figure 5C, a male housefly 7 days old with at least

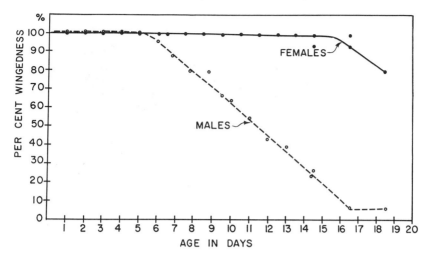

Fig. 3. Age-related wing loss in male and female houseflies (Rockstein & Brandt 1963).

60% of the wings lost by abrading. Finally, in Figure 5D, there is seen a housefly with what we consider complete wing loss; that is, more than 50% of the wing area has been lost by fraying. In most cases, male houseflies more than 2 weeks old are flightless and vary only slightly in external appearance, from possessing very short stubbles of wings to being completely wingless.

The Nobel Laureaute, Sumner, once described life as an "orderly functioning of enzymes"; conversely, failure of a system or of a function can, I believe, be rationalized in terms of failure of some enzyme systems on the one hand, or, perhaps less likely, the abnormal or excessive production of others, on the other hand. My experimental research has therefore stressed the quantitative estimation of changes in key enzymes in organs or tissues showing patent alteration in structure and gross function with age from very young age to mature to senile old age.

In my earlier studies (Rockstein 1959b). I had found that, concomitant with *maturation* of flight ability, there occurred the biochemical event, namely, an *increase* in the brain enzyme, acetylcholine esterase, as well as in other enzyme systems. An attempt was therefore made to determine what changes occur in these and other key enzyme systems in the flight muscle of the aging male housefly, an unusually good model for aging studies, in view of this age-related failure in flight ability. Figure 6 (Rockstein & Brandt 1963) shows

Fig. 4. Age-related wing loss in female houseflies. A. Newly emerged female 5 minutes old—wings are still unexpanded. B. Female 30 minutes old—wings are fully expanded. C. Female 4 days old—wings completely intact. D. Female 18 days old—some abrading and fraying of the outer margin of both wings is evident.

the time-related changes in intramitochondrial magnesium-activated ATP-ase activity, which continues to rise after the animal has emerged as a fully winged adult. The peak of activity is seen to be reached between the fourth to fifth day, with a sharp decline to very old age. Concomitantly, the ATP content of flight muscle first reaches its lowest level at the time of the peak of the magnesium-activated ATP-ase activity. Conversely, it rises dramatically at the same point where the enzyme has fallen precipitously, namely, at the ninth to tenth day (Table 1; Clark & Rockstein 1964). As can also be seen

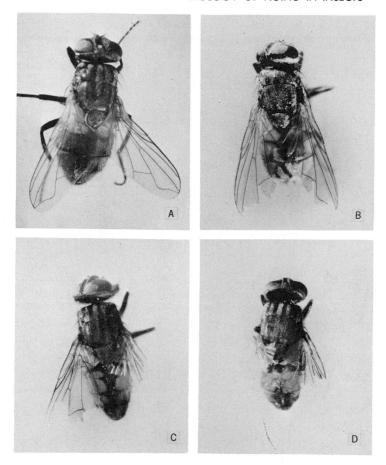

Fig. 5. Age-related wing loss in male houseflies. A. Male housefly 30 min. old. B. Male housefly 4 days old—outer margins of wings showing onset of abrading. C. Male housefly 7 days old—costal, outer, and inner wing margins all showing pronounced abrading. D. Male housefly 18 days old—both wings severely abraded, left wing almost totally gone.

from Table 1, the AMP and ADP content of the thorax correspondingly fall dramatically during this latter period of adult male life, thus showing a reciprocal quantitative relationship to the ATP content.

That these biochemical and structural correlates of aging in the housefly are not unique to insects is seen from the data, published by Rockstein & Brandt (1961, 1962), on the related changes in structure and in the biochemical components of the skeletal (gastroc-

Table 1. Mg-activated ATP-ase activity and adenine nucleotide content of flight muscle of aging male house flies, *Musca domestica* L.[a]

Age	Enzyme activity	AMP	ADP	ATP
0–2 hr	0.065	3.9	1.2	1.0
6–8 hr	—	4.4	1.1	0.7
22–24 hr	0.075	5.7	0.8	1.6
44–48 hr	0.082	5.3	0.9	0.8
3–4 days	0.095	4.9	0.4	0.6
4–5 days	0.102	6.6	0.5	1.9
6–7 days	0.107	4.6	1.6	2.7
7–8 days	0.096	—	—	—
8–9 days	0.087	1.2	2.0	6.7
12–13 days	0.064	1.8	2.2	5.2
14–15 days	0.062	1.7	1.8	5.2
15–16 days	0.060	1.1	1.3	6.2

[a] Enzyme activity is expressed as γP released/fly/10 min incubation; adenine nucleotide is expressed in absorbance units per total extract from 50 thoraces, at each age (Clark & Rockstein 1964).

nemius) muscle of aging male Sprague-Dawley and CFN white rats. Thus, in the case of the Sprague-Dawley animals, the pronounced changes in muscle mass from 4.58 to 2.45 g, from approximately 9 months of age to approximately 26 months of age, respectively, is accompanied by the decline (on a *muscle mass* basis) of ATP-ase activity from 0.69 μg of phosphorus, for the youngest group of animals, to 0.24 μg of phosphorus released/15 min/g of fresh muscle mass, in the old group of animals. This represents a loss of approximately two-thirds of the original activity. Moreover, in the case of male Sprague-Dawley animals, the very old rat shows a typical "muscular dystrophy-like syndrome" which accompanies this pronounced loss in muscle mass as well as in ATP-ase activity. On the other hand, old CFN animals show a much smaller loss both in muscle mass as well as in ATP-ase activity on a fresh muscle weight basis, so that the muscle mass is essentially unchanged from 7 months to approximately 30 months of age, whereas the ATP-ase activity falls from 0.8 to approximately 0.4 μg of phosphorus/15 min/g of fresh muscle mass. Accompanying this much smaller loss in ATP-ase activity and no change in muscle mass with advancing age is the absence of the muscular dystrophy-like syndrome in the much longer-lived CFN animals.

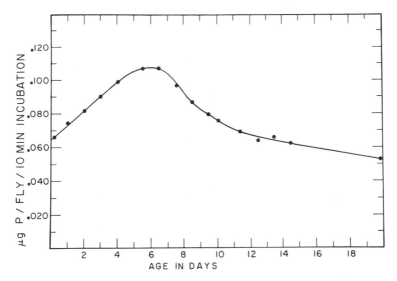

Fig. 6. Mitochondrial Mg-activated ATP-ase activity in aging male houseflies (from Rockstein & Brandt 1963).

In the strong flying insects, the otherwise fairly universal pathway for intermediary metabolism of carbohydrates, typical of higher animals, as well as of bacteria in part, is marked by a peculiar aberrancy in one specific instance. This is the presence in the sarcoplasm of the enzyme alpha-glycerophosphate dehydrogenase as that enzyme responsible for the restoration of NAD (DPN) from the reduced form, thus making available the oxidized form of NAD for the important chemical reactions concerned with the synthesis of high-energy containing phosphorus compounds (ATP) (Figure 7; Clark & Rockstein 1964). This has as its well-known vertebrate counterpart (especially in skeletal muscle) lactic acid dehydrogenase. Estimated at a pH of 8.6, this enzyme system (Figure 8; Rockstein & Brandt 1963) shows a gradual increase during the first 3 days of adult life in the male housefly and then proceeds to diminish at 3 to 4 days of age (actually at 36 to 48 hr before wing loss and the initial onset of decline in ATP-ase activity). This decline in activity is quite pronounced from about 72 hr to about 10 days of age and then continues to fall at a slow, steady, but still very gradual rate throughout the remaining life-span of the adult male housefly.

As a result of these earlier and more recent observations on the housefly, the obvious question arose as to the cause-and-effect relationship of this precursor biochemical event (namely, the decline in alpha-

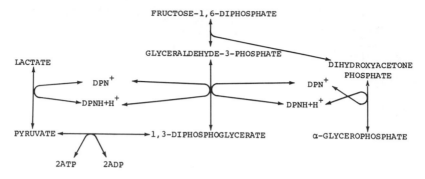

Fig. 7. Pathways of oxidation of reduced NAD (DPN) in vertebrates and in flying insects (after Clark & Rockstein 1964).

glycerophosphate dehydrogenase activity) and the failure of flight, particularly wing loss, since failure in the activity of this enzyme *precedes* the actual loss of wings per se. I therefore undertook a number of experiments in which the surgical removal of the wings from newly-emerged houseflies was followed by the observation of any changes in life-span, as well as in the activity of those two enzyme systems, for which we had previously obtained some correlation with loss of wings.

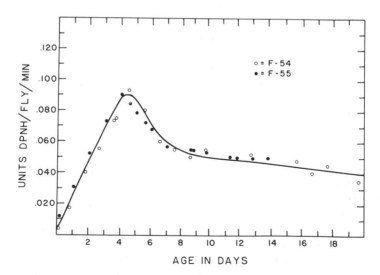

Fig. 8. Alpha-glycerophosphate dehydrogenase activity of aging male houseflies (from Rockstein & Brandt 1963).

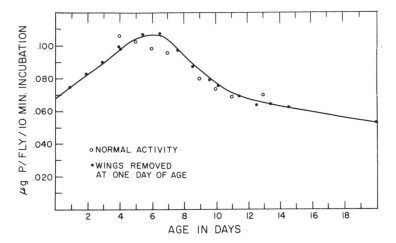

Fig. 9. Mg-activated ATP-ase activity in normal and de-alated male houseflies.

Figure 9 shows that the removal of wings before the normal onset of aging (i.e., in the newly-emerged housefly) results in virtually no change in the age-related pattern of magnesium-activated ATP-ase. On the other hand, Figure 10 shows that such surgical removal of the wings from the very young male fly (i.e., prior to its actual attainment of maturity of flight ability) blocks the otherwise normal decline in such alpha-glycerophosphate dehydrogenase activity; i.e.,

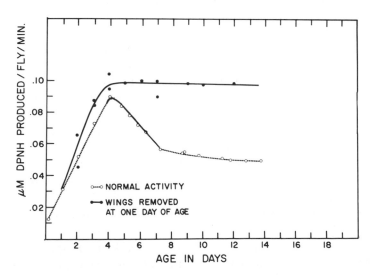

Fig. 10. Alpha-glycerophosphate dehydrogenase activity in normal and de-alated male houseflies.

the peak level attained at 36 hrs of age persists at least through the fourteenth day of adult life in the case of the males, a point where normally 90% of the adult males will have lost their wings and the enzyme would be at close to its minimum level of activity. Thus, in the artificially-produced wingless fly, this enzyme system remains at its peak level once this level has been reached. This observation suggests very strongly that the very presence of the intact wing of normal flies in some (direct or indirect) fashion is responsible for the ultimate failure of a vital enzyme system, alpha-glycerophosphate dehydrogenase, and thus for the ultimate *loss of the wings* themselves. This may involve a higher center, perhaps endocrine in origin, which negatively feeds back from the intact wing of the normal young fly to inhibit or reduce production of the enzyme and thus result in the failure of flight. Similar but less striking data have been obtained in recent de-alation studies on female houseflies, where one also finds (Figure 11) a direct relationship between mitochondrial magnesium-activated ATP-ase activity levels and the degree of retention of flight ability (particularly, intactness of wings).

In order to pinpoint more precisely the site of such changes at the cytological level, we have also been studying the intimate structural changes in flight muscle of aging flies, particularly the size and number of the giant mitochondria or sarcosomes.

Table 2 (Rockstein & Bhatnagar 1965) shows that the number of flight muscle mitochondria in the male fly reaches a maximum by the eighth day of adult life, levels off until the eleventh to twelfth day, and then begins to fall steadily. This is similarly true of the female housefly in which the number of mitochondria also reach a maximum by the eighth day of adult life, with a slow decline thereafter to a fairly low minimum in very old females. However, de-alation does not alter appreciably the agewise pattern of distribution of mitochondrial *number,* in either male or female houseflies, with a maximum number occurring somewhere between the seventh to eighth day in such de-alated flies just as in the case of such normal flies. The size of the giant mitochondria likewise gradually increases from emergence so as to reach a maximum somewhere around the eighth day of adult life, with a slow decline thereafter (Table 3, Rockstein & Bhatnagar 1965), both in normal as well as in de-alated males and females.

Thus, de-alation appears to have no marked or appreciable influence upon either mitochondrial number or size with age, both in males and in females.

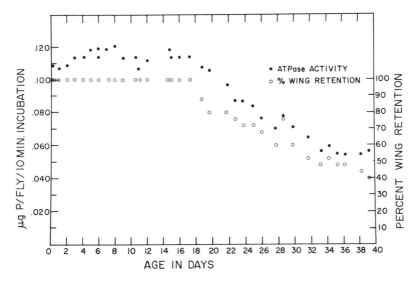

Fig. 11. Mg-activated ATP-ase activity in relation to wing retention in normal, aging female houseflies (from Clark & Rockstein 1964).

Table 2. Number of mitochondria in the flight muscle of aging house flies

	Number ($\times 10^7$)			
	Per male		Per female	
Age	Normal	De-alated	Normal	De-alated
4 hr	13.71	13.29	12.02	11.38
24 hr	14.41	14.36	12.73	11.52
3 days	14.63	15.39	20.10	19.06
4 days	14.56	15.44	20.04	19.37
6 days	16.01	15.11	20.06	19.60
7 days	17.43	18.88	20.14	19.39
8 days	19.78	—	20.20	—
11 days	19.31	18.41	19.88	18.65
12 days	19.32	—	19.89	—
14 days	16.45	15.04	19.40	18.74
15 days	15.44	—	19.44	—
16 days	—	14.89	—	17.52
19 days	14.24	13.01	19.14	17.25
20 days	—	—	18.74	—
21 days	13.23	13.23	15.24	15.41
24 days	—	—	15.32	—
25 days	—	—	—	14.10
27 days	—	—	12.76	12.68

Table 3. Changes in the size of the giant mitochondria in the flight muscle of aging houseflies

| | Size (in μ) | | | |
| | Males | | Females | |
Age	Normal	De-alated	Normal	De-alated
4 hr	1.92	1.99	1.88	1.89
24 hr	1.91	1.98	1.94	2.06
3 days	2.04	2.00	2.12	2.11
4 days	2.08	2.07	2.13	2.14
5 days	—	2.18	—	2.08
6 days	2.10	2.14	2.18	2.21
7 days	2.11	2.14	2.28	2.29
8 days	2.28	—	2.37	—
9 days	—	2.28	—	2.39
11 days	2.12	2.18	2.23	2.19
14 days	2.06	2.07	2.26	2.19
15 days	1.96	—	2.24	—
16 days	—	1.92	—	2.13
19 days	1.96	1.92	2.25	2.08
21 days	1.95	1.89	1.95	2.02
24 days	—	—	1.92	—
25 days	—	—	—	1.86
27 days	—	—	1.89	—

In the relatively early days of our knowledge of insect biochemistry, it was commonly accepted that the reserve energy carbohydrate for flight was glycogen. This was based on a number of important reports including those by Chadwick & Gilmour (1940), by Williams, Barness & Sawyer 1943), and by Wigglesworth (1949). However, later reports by Wyatt & Kalf (1957), as well as those by Howden & Kilby (1956), by Evans & Dethier (1957), and by Clegg & Evans (1961a) confirm the fact that the nonreducing disaccharide, trehalose, is found in high concentrations in the hemolymph, especially in insects possessing flight muscles capable of contracting at very rapid rates for long periods of time, like the Diptera. Moreover, the most recent report by Clegg & Evans (1961b) clearly established the role of trehalose as a primary carbohydrate source for the function of flight by showing a direct relationship between wing beat frequency and concentration of blood trehalose (Figure 12) in *Phormia regina*. Even more recently, the presence of the enzyme trehalase, capable of

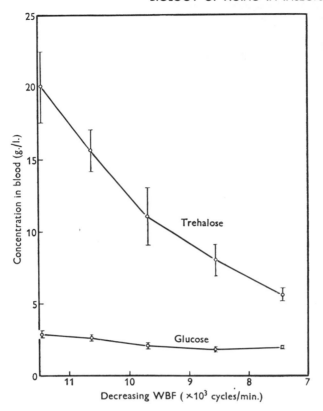

Fig. 12. The relation of wing beat frequency to trehalose blood concentration in *Phormia regina* (from Clegg & Evans 1961a).

rapid liberation of glucose from trehalose, has been demonstrated in the blood of the fly *Phormia regina* by Friedman (1960).

At the present time, our laboratory is therefore concerned with the demonstration of a likely correlation between the blood trehalose content in aging houseflies and the concomitant structural and functional decline in the motor function of flight in this particular model species of senescence.

Finally a recent study with Dr. Hawkins has shown that still another biochemical component, thiamine, exhibits an age-related distribution corresponding almost precisely to the age changes in thoracic flight muscle alpha-glycerophosphate dehydrogenase. Thus, Figure 13 shows a rapid rise in thiamine content in the male thorax to a maximum at 3 to 4 days which is followed by a rapid fall to the ninth day and a more gradual falling off thereafter.

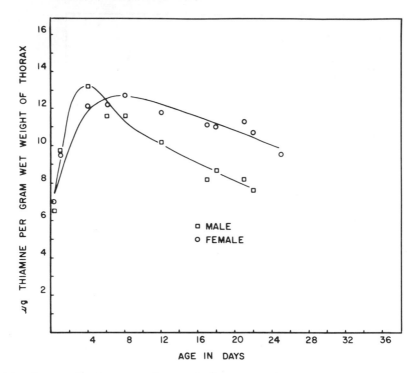

Fig. 13. Age-related content of thiamine in isolated housefly thoraces (Rockstein & Hawkins unpublished).

In the female, with the peak level of thiamine being reached by the seventh to eighth day, the decline thereafter is much more gradual, again paralleling the much slower loss in flight ability which is characteristic of the normally aging female.

Thus, the evidence for underlying biochemical mechanisms related to, if not responsible for, the aging of the motor function of flight in insects continues to accumulate slowly. This may give some support to the concept that in senescence, errors are occurring in the cell, such that the structure of the DNA molecule is altered (whether by irradiation or by intrinsic environmental influences), and these errors are transmissible via messenger RNA to the enzymes normally being synthesized. However, considering the relative importance of the endocrines in governing growth, development, and differentiation, one should also study in the complex multicellular organism the time-dependent changes in endocrine function which may, in fact, govern or control the observed changes in the senescent organs (which may be considered the target organs of the endocrine glands which are themselves aging) .

To seek ultimates is the goal of all scholars; to the experimental gerontologist, the study of the aging process has the continuing challenge of seeking answers at more and more intimate levels, once the first clue has been obtained. My own long-term studies of aging of the flight muscle in the common housefly have led me further and further to the necessity of studying mechanisms as well as parameters of the aging process.

Acknowledgment

The original research discussed in the report was supported in part by funds from Grants #GM 9680 and #HD 00571 from the National Institutes of Health.

References

Chadwick, L. E., and Gilmour, D. (1940). *Physiol. Zool. 13*, 398–410.

Clark, A. M. and Rockstein, M. (1964). In *The Physiology of Insecta*, Rockstein, M., Ed. Academic Press, New York, p. 227–281.

Clegg, J. S. and Evans, D. R. (1961a). *J. Exp. Biol., 38*, 771–792.

Clegg, J. S. and Evans, D. R. (1961b). *Science, 134*, 54–55.

Evans, D. R. and Dethier, V. G. (1957) . *J. Insect Physiol., 3*, 118–120.

Friedman, S. (1960). *Arch. Biochem., 87*, 252–258.

Howden, G. F. and Kilby, B. A. (1956). *Chem. and Industr. (Rev.)*, 1453–1454.

Levenbook, L. and Williams, C. M. (1956). *J. Gen. Physiol., 39*, 497–512.

Rockstein, M. (1957). *J. Geront., 12*, 253–256.

Rockstein, M. (1959a). In *The Lifespan of Animals, Ciba Foundation Colloquia on Ageing*, Wolstenholme, G. E. W. and O'Connor, M., Eds., Vol. 5, Little, Brown & Co., p. 247–264.

Rockstein, M. (1959b). *Smithsonian Inst. Misc. Collections, 137*, 263–286.

Rockstein, M. (1960). In *The Biology of Aging*, Strehler, B. L., et al., Eds., Waverly Press, Baltimore, p. 243–245.

Rockstein, M. and Bhatnagar, P. L., (1965). *J. Insect Physiol., 11*, 481–491.

Rockstein, M. and Brandt, K. F. (1961). *Proc. Soc. Exp. Biol. and Med., 107*, 377–380.

Rockstein, M. and Brandt, K. F. (1962). *Nature, 196*, 142–143.

Rockstein, M. and Brandt, K. F. (1963). *Science, 139*, 1049–1051.

Rockstein, M. and Lieberman, H. S. (1959). *Gerontologia, 3*, 23–36.

Sacktor, B. (1953a). *Arch. Biochem., 45*, 349–365.

Sacktor, B. (1953b). *J. Gen. Physiol., 36*, 371–387.

Sacktor, B. (1954). *J. Gen. Physiol., 37*, 343–359.

Sacktor, B. (1961). *Ann. Rev. Entom., 6*, 103–130.

Watanabe, M. I. and Williams, C. M. (1951). *J. Gen Physiol., 34*, 675–689.

Watanabe, M. I. and Williams, C. M. (1953). *J. Gen. Physiol., 37*, 71–90.

Wigglesworth, V. B. (1949). *J. Exp. Biol.*, 26, 150–163.

Wigglesworth, V. B. (1950). In *The Principles of Insect Physiology*, Methuen & Co., London, pp. 95–110.

Williams, C. M., Barness, L. A. and Sawyer, W. H. (1943). *Biol. Bull.*, *84*, 263–272.

Williams, C. M. and Williams, M. V. (1943). *J. Morph.*, *72*, 589–599.

Wyatt, G. R. and Kalf, G. F. (1957). *J. Gen. Physiol.*, *40*, 833–849.

DISCUSSION

DR. SALK: Do the males fly more than the females?

DR. ROCKSTEIN: No. In my first publication on the aging of the housefly I mentioned that the males lost their wings. For a long time no one had ever observed this in the laboratory because in most laboratories the houseflies are used for insecticide assays, and are not kept for more than 4 to 5 days. It has been claimed by some that the male's wings began to wear out because of the resistance of the female to the male's second attempts at copulation. However, the phenomenon is found in isolated males as well.

A study on wing beat frequency with age shows that the difference between the sexes is not a matter of higher frequency or greater length of duration of flight.

DR. SINEX: What is the male's resistance to mechanical stress? Is his wing not as good mechanically?

DR. ROCKSTEIN: The nature of the aging wing, which is primarily extracellular material, is a problem for the connective tissue people to study.

DR. BOURNE: Is there any physiological change in connective tissue of the muscle as it gets older?

DR. ROCKSTEIN: We have not done any histological studies, but we have gone to the intracellular elements, to mitochondria.

DR. ORGEL: Are the flies that have more than the median amount of the enzyme the ones most likely to survive?

DR. ROCKSTEIN: I can only guess so. The retention of wings is certainly a very good marker for longevity.

DR. MAYNARD SMITH: In drosophila experiments the flies do not fly, whereas your houseflies do fly. Are you sure that the difference between males and females does not actually reflect a difference in activity? Can one define an activity index in terms of how rapidly they beat their wings and how much time is spent flying?

DR. ROCKSTEIN: I doubt if a fly of 53 days of age is flying. She hops about but she finds the food, she is old, and she has an oedematous-like appearance in the abdomen; the abdomen is translucent.

DR. MAYNARD SMITH: It would be very interesting to know whether the changes, both in the wings falling off and in enzymes, are affected by the use of the muscle. If the muscle is not being used so much perhaps it behaves differently. I find it hard to see how one could record the activity of an insect but it is not an insuperable problem.

Do you have a mutant gene in houseflies like vestigial or wingless? It would be very handy.

DR. ROCKSTEIN: No. But vestigial drosophila should be studied.

DR. BOURNE: In the rat study did you find the drop in ATP only in animals which show the dystrophy-like syndrome?

DR. ROCKSTEIN: The very pronounced form was found in all the old animals; all the old males showed a drag in performance.

DR. KOHN: Is this calcium-activated enzyme?

DR. ROCKSTEIN: No, this is a magnesium-activated enzyme. This is not the actomyosin system; we found no appreciable changes in the actomyosin, which we looked at concurrently.

The figures in Table 1 are for the entire gastrocnemius muscle, specifically, which is a fast muscle.

DR. KOHN: Did you look in the serum for this enzyme? Could this be a leakage phenomenon of the muscle or is this a defect in synthesis?

DR. ROCKSTEIN: When you say serum, the muscle preparation is best described as being frozen, crushed, and then extracted in cold buffered solution from this point on.

DR. KOHN: One wants to know whether this enzyme is not being synthesized or is leaking out. In muscular dystrophy there is a leakage of enzymes from a change in permeability of the sarcolemma.

DR. ROCKSTEIN: All we can do is relate either to DNA (which we have not done) or to mass which we have done in the case of the rat, or, in the case of the insect, to the actual number of mitochondria which we have done indirectly. There is some evidence here for the concept of an error occurring in the cell and it is reasonable to think that we are dealing with a lower production per unit of mass of material in the cell.

DR. KOHN: This is the most striking example I have seen of an age-related loss of enzymatic function in this type of cell. Are there any other soluble proteins which behave in the same way?

DR. ROCKSTEIN: We are completing a study of lactic dehydrogenase in the skeletal muscle of the Sprague-Dawley rat. We have tried this on another strain of rat and there was no change with age. In the case of the Sprague-Dawley male, there is no change with age either, so that the counterpart of the alpha-glycerophosphate dehydrogenase (lactic dehydrogenase) in the skeletal muscle of the same strain of rat does not appear to show age-dependent senescence.

DR. SALLMAN: We have looked at some soluble enzymes (LDH) in the rabbit heart. There are major differences when one compares a 6 to 9 month old rabbit with a 6 or 7 year old rabbit.

DR. BIRREN: I am interested in the fact that the Sprague-Dawley rat showed the enzyme change and the other strain did not.

DR. ROCKSTEIN: The CFN strain did show this but not as dramatically. It is just that the relative difference (of 45% and 60%) correlates more or less with the difference in the longevity and in failure of the motor ability.

DR. BIRREN: There is the possibility that in the Sprague-Dawley rat one has a specific genetic defect, a neuro-muscular dystrophy of some sort. This would be an epiphenomenon and not one of the intrinsic processes of aging.

THE ROLE OF SOMATIC MUTATIONS IN AGING*

Howard J. Curtis

Department of Biology,
Brookhaven National Laboratory,
Upton, New York

It is by now quite clear that aging is a condition separate and distinct from the symptoms by which it is usually described. Thus cancer incidence increases with chronological age, as do most of the degenerative diseases, but it is a result of aging rather than its cause. Something happens to the organism which increases the probability of contracting one of these degenerative diseases. Since the death rate from all causes increases exponentially with age, the conquest of one of these would increase the human life expectancy very little. Thus if all cancer could be completely cured, the average life expectancy would be increased only 1.5 years. The dramatic conquest of the infectious diseases caused a spectacular increase in average life expectancy, but the maximum life-span of man has not changed during recorded history. It thus appears that if something is to be accomplished in materially lengthening the human life-span a completely different approach must be undertaken. Certainly the first step in such a program is to achieve an understanding of the nature of the aging process.

It seems to be customary to consider that aging is identical in all biological systems, and if one understands the process for one, he can translate this to all others. This is certainly a false concept. In the first place, aging is a consequence of differentiation, so we must exclude all undifferentiated forms from consideration. Beyond this, all systems go through some sort of life cycle, and one part of the cycle usually corresponds in a superficial way to what we refer to as aging in the human. But the basic process may be completely different. The aging of a tree, for example, probably bears very little resemblance to aging in man. There are certainly many different facets to the aging problem, and whereas basic biological truths undoubtedly

* Research carried out at Brookhaven National Laboratory under the auspices of the U.S. Atomic Energy Commission.

apply to all systems, different facets play such different roles in the different plants and animals that they appear to be quite different phenomena. This paper does not permit a discussion of comparative aging, but a few words of caution should be sounded. It should not be concluded from experiments on one species that one theory of aging is proven or disproven. It is erroneous to conclude from experiments on planaria or drosophila that "the" cause of aging in man follows one or another path. I should hasten to add that such experiments can be extremely interesting, but they should be interpreted with caution.

By the same token, it seems almost certain now that different organs in a mammal age at different rates and for different reasons. Thus even for a single species of animal there is certainly no one cause of aging. It is a complex process and should be treated as such.

In the present treatment I shall confine my attention to aging in the mammal, and draw on information from other forms only insofar as it has a bearing on the mammalian problem.

CELLULAR AGING

The old controversy about whether or not individual cells age has finally been resolved; they do age. Evidence favoring this view comes from a number of sources. The genetic information in the somatic cells, as contained in the DNA molecules, controls the function of the individual cell. Indeed from what we now know it appears that the only way in which a permanent change, short of death, can be affected in the cell is by a change in the DNA or chromosome structure. All other damage can be repaired. A change in the DNA of a cell is referred to as a mutation, whether the cell is a somatic or a germ cell and whether or not it ever undergoes division again. If a somatic cell undergoes mutation, it is a different cell designed to perform a different function. However, if a change occurs in a somatic cell in a character not necessary for the function of that cell, then the consequences will be unimportant. For example, if the gene for eye color is mutated in a liver cell, nothing of consequence will result. But if the gene controlling the synthesis of an essential enzyme is altered, the cell will no longer perform its function well. As will be discussed later, somatic cells undergo mutation at quite a high rate, and if they do not undergo division, they must deteriorate. If they do undergo division, the mutated cells will be at a selective disadvantage and be eliminated from the organ. In such an organ one might consider that the cells were "young" even in an old animal in the same sense that the cells of a bacterial suspension are perpetually young.

In the mammal it is found that chromosome aberrations, which can be taken as an index of mutations, do not accumulate in white blood cells (Bender & Gooch 1962), so from this point of view organs such as the bone marrow do not age. Obviously, if a mutation were to occur in one of these cells which gave it a selective advantage, or at least no selective disadvantage, in cell division, it would not be eliminated. Many people feel this is a very likely mechanism of cancer induction.

Chromosome aberrations do accumulate in mammalian liver cells, reaching values as high as 75% in some old mice (Crowley & Curtis 1963). Thus one could legitimately say that mammalian cells such as those of the liver do age.

Another indication of the aging of individual cells comes from work with tissue culture. Hayflick (1965) has shown that cells from various organs grown in tissue culture are able to undergo about 50 cell divisions before they go to pieces and die, unless a change has taken place in the culture which essentially transforms it into a cancer. Furthermore, if the cells are taken from an old animal, they are unable to go through as many divisions as are the cells from a young animal. This is quite convincing evidence that something happens to the individual cells to cause them gradually to deteriorate. There is at least some evidence indicating that it may be the accumulation of mutations in these cells which causes their eventual demise.

In an interesting series of experiments Krohn (1963) repeatedly grafted the same piece of mouse skin, originally derived from a young mouse, onto other young mice. A certain interval was allowed between each re-grafting, so the piece of skin grew old while the hosts stayed young. In this way he was able to keep the piece of skin alive longer than the maximum life-span of a mouse, but not very much. In spite of the most careful technique, the skin would deteriorate and eventually die. Again it would be satisfying to postulate that mutations were accumulating in the piece of skin, but there is no evidence to either support or deny this explanation.

These experiments show that mutations build up in nondividing cells of the mammal as a function of time, and also strongly imply that mutations which may have a selective advantage, or at least no selective disadvantage, in cell division build up in dividing cells. Thus with the passage of time the cell nucleus, the "master organ" of the cell, deteriorates. One is certainly justified in speaking of this as cellular aging. The question now is whether this is actually causally associated with the aging process of the whole animal, or a concomitant symptom such as graying of the hair.

MUTATIONS AND AGING

There is no known method of measuring mutations in individual somatic cells. However, one can examine mitotic figures microscopically and detect aberrations in them. For the white blood cells this is done by arresting the divisions in metaphase with colchicine. For the normally nondividing cells of the body, one can force the liver cells into division by a partial hepatectomy, and observe microscopically the cells in anaphase or telophase. Abnormalities, if present, will show up at this point, and cells can be scored as either normal or abnormal (Stevenson & Curtis 1961). It can be shown that this can be taken as an index of the mutations present in these cells.

One of the most convincing experiments showing a causal relation between mutations and aging compares the rate of development of mutations in liver cells of a short-lived versus a long-lived strain of mice (Crowley & Curtis 1963). The results (Figure 1) show that the short-lived strain develop mutations at a much faster rate than the long-lived one, implying that the short-lived strain ages faster because it develops mutations faster. These two strains are ones in which the individuals die from a variety of different causes so one can feel some confidence that the differences in life-span reflect differences in physiological aging, and not a specific defect.

Another very recent experiment reinforcing this idea compares the rate of development of mutations in dogs and mice (Curtis, Leith & Tilley 1966). One could reason that liver cells in dogs are about the same and perform about the same functions as the same cells in mice so they should develop mutations at about the same rate. On the other hand, mice age about six times faster than dogs, so if mutations and aging are correlated, mutations should develop six times faster in mice. The experiment (Figure 2) shows the latter to be true, so cells age at the same rate as does the animal of which they are part, and again one would imply a causal relationship.

It should be pointed out that there are exceptions to the rule that the longest lived animals develop mutations at the slowest rate. Recent experiments (Curtis, Tilley, Crowley & Fuller 1966) show that if the C58 strain of mouse is compared with the 129 strain, the rate

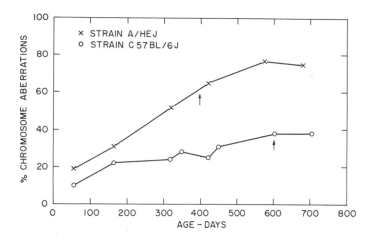

Fig. 1. Chromosome aberrations in liver cells of two inbred strains of mice, plotted as a function of age. The median life-span of each strain is indicated by the arrows (from Crowley & Curtis 1963).

of development of mutations is about the same for each, yet the mice of strain C58 almost all died of leukemia at about 12 months of age, while strain 129 is a very long-lived strain. Apparently a single gene mutation in strain C58 causes leukemia, leaving the susceptibility to other diseases unchanged.

Another similar experiment was attempted to determine the genetic basis for chromosomal stability (Curtis, Tilley, Crowley & Fuller 1966). Mice from a long-lived strain, C57BL/6J, were crossed with those from a short-lived strain, A/HeJ. In general the hybrids will be longer lived than either of the parent strains. However, in this instance this was not quite the case, although they were much longer lived than the short lived parents. The rate of development of chromosome aberrations in liver cells tended to follow inversely the life expectancy of the individuals, but the correlation was not exact.

These experiments show that there are factors involved in aging other than mutations. The experiments of Tannenbaum & Silverstone (1953) show what at least one of the factors must be. They showed that the development of a tumor is greatly influenced by the diet of the animal. He was able to postpone the development of an induced tumor almost indefinitely by the proper diet. Thus one can easily imagine that a change in the eating habits of mice, due to a slight hereditary change, could alter the consequences of the mutations and thus alter the longevity without altering the chromosome stability. There is still a very great deal to learn about factors, such as diet,

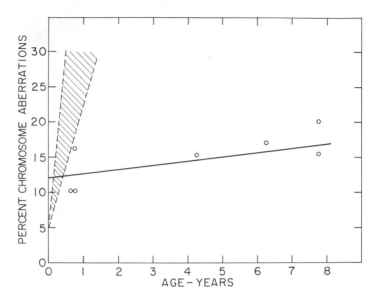

Fig. 2. Chromosome aberrations in liver cells of dogs plotted as a function of age. The shaded area within the dotted lines indicates the limits, plotted on the same scales, of all strains of mice so far investigated by this method (from Curtis, Leith & Tilley 1966).

which alter the life expectancy. For example, mice of a very pure strain may have quite different life expectancies in two different well-run laboratories for reasons which are almost completely unknown.

From these experiments it seems reasonable to conclude that there is a general correlation between the rate of development of chromosomal aberrations (chromosome stability) and longevity. It remains to examine the effect on this stability of agents which affect the rate of aging.

RADIATIONS AND AGING

It has been known for many years that ionizing radiations shorten the life expectancy of animals in a way which closely resembles accelerated aging. The tumor spectrum is about the same for irradiated mice as for their controls, but the tumors appear at a younger age in the former. The same holds true for nephrosclerosis and amyloidosis (see Lindop & Rotblat 1961). There are a few minor exceptions to this general rule known, and more will undoubtedly be

found. Since aging in the mammal is an exceedingly complex reaction, it would be miraculous if an agent could be found that would
affect all facets of the process equally, and the wonder is that radiation affects as many as it does. It can thus be used as a very potent
tool for studying the aging process.

When the effect of radiation on chromosome aberrations in regenerating liver cells is examined, a remarkable correspondence is
found. First, as shown in Figure 3, the aberrations increase immediately following a dose of X-rays and decline slowly over a period
of many months (Stevenson & Curtis 1961). The amount of the increase is proportional to the dose, as is the degree of shortening of
the life span.

It is well known that for X- or gamma-rays, if the radiation is
given very slowly over a long period of time, a given dose will be
only about one quarter as effective as will the same dose administered acutely. Thus 2000 rads of gamma-rays, when given at a low
dose rate over several months, will produce, in mice, about the same
effect as a single acute dose of 500 rads. When this same effect is
investigated for chromosome aberrations, the same relation is found to
hold (Curtis & Crowley 1963) (Figure 4); for chronic irradiation the
aberrations increase only about one quarter as fast as one would
expect on the basis of acute exposure data.

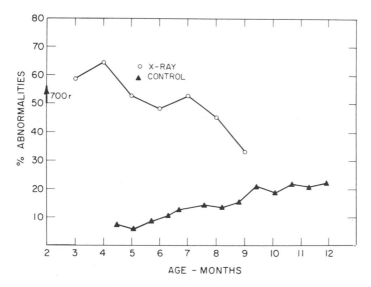

Fig. 3. Chromosome aberrations in liver cells as a function of age in normal mice
and in mice which had received a large dose of X-rays (from Stevenson & Curtis
1961).

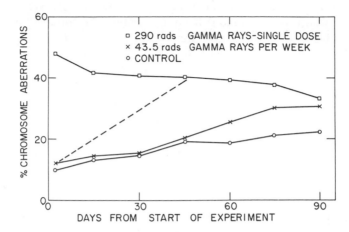

Fig. 4. Chromosome aberrations in liver cells of mice (×) subjected continuously to gamma irradiation, (□) given a large dose of gamma-rays, and (○) un-treated controls. The dashed line shows the rate of build-up of aberrations which would be expected on theoretical grounds if low dose rate irradiation were as effec-tive as is a single acute dose. From the difference in slope between the experi-mental and theoretical curves, it can be estimated that chronic is only about 25% as effective in producing aberrations as is acute irradiation, indicating that for very small doses of radiation about 75% of the chromosomal damage can be repaired (from Curtis, Tilley & Crowley 1964).

Again, it is known that the shortening of the life-span for neutron irradiation depends only on dose, and is independent of the dose rate. The same is found to be true for chromosome aberrations (Curtis, Tilley & Crowley 1964) (Figure 5). This leads to the con-cept that the dense ionization caused locally by neutron irradiation leads to damage to the chromosomes too severe to be repaired. This can also be observed in Figure 5 in that, following a single dose of neutrons, there is very little return of the aberration frequency toward the control values. These studies have been carried on for about 18 months following a single dose of neutrons, and still there was only a slight suggestion of a repair of the damage.

It can be stated categorically that for all different radiations and radiation regimes so far investigated, there is a good correspondence between the induction of aberrations in liver cells and the shortening of the life-span (Curtis 1963). It would be surprising if there were not a causal relation between them.

These experiments show, as have many others, that there is an active repair of chromosomal damage following injury. Certainly this repair process must operate on spontaneous mutations as well as

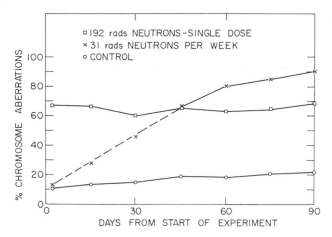

Fig. 5. Chromosome aberrations in liver cells of mice (□) given a large single dose of neutrons, (×) subjected to neutron irradiation at a low dose rate, and (O) untreated controls. The dashed line shows the rate of build-up of chromosome aberrations which would be expected on theoretical grounds if low dose rate irradiation were as effective as is a single acute dose. The experimental points fall so close to the theoretical line that the assumption would seem justified. This indicates that for this radiation, which produces discrete tracks of heavy ionization in the tissue causing extensive localized chromosomal damage, when a chromosome is hit there can be no repair (from Curtis, Tilley & Crowley 1964).

induced ones, as shown principally by work on bacteria. Thus our present picture of the chromosomes is of a labile structure which is continually breaking down and repairing itself. A few of the breaks are so large as to be irreparable, and it is this class of breaks which apparently persists to cause aging. The dividing cells of the body apparently are just as susceptible to mutation as any other kind, but they have very little time for repair between divisions. But the selection process during cell division eliminates most of the cells carrying aberrations, leaving a tissue reasonably free of mutation.

LIMITATIONS OF THE THEORY

These experiments argue strongly in favor of the mutation theory of aging, but at the same time point up many limitations and difficulties. First, it is not easy to understand the long delay between the production of mutations and their manifestation in terms of increased death rate. Actually the age-specific death rate starts to increase within a month or two following irradiation, in mice, and remains elevated for the remaining life-span of the group.

This delay can, perhaps, be explained by assuming that the cells are functioning on the stored RNA and protein, but this would require most RNA to have a lifetime far longer than most of the lifetimes recorded so far for mammalian systems. However, there are other experiments using arbacia eggs, bacteria, cells in culture, etc., which show that cells can continue to live and divide for considerable periods with all or part of their DNA damaged. Thus there seems little difficulty in accepting the idea of a long delay even if the mechanism remains in some doubt.

The quantitative aspects of the problems are also troublesome. It would be very satisfying if one could say that a certain time after the induction of some number of mutations the probability of death would be increased by a certain amount. However, it is apparent that it is not that simple, but the nature of the relationship remains obscure.

It seems that the simple assumption made by Szilard (1959) is that death is imminent when both genes, in a diploid organism, controlling an essential function, finally become inactivated. The experiments reported here show that this concept is untenable in its present form. The chief experiment showing this involves giving a large dose of radiation to old mice, in which case no change in the life expectancy is observed. But according to Szilard's hypothesis the radiation should be more, not less, effective when the animals are old.

These difficulties indicate problems which are awaiting attack, and as their solutions are achieved will no doubt cause modifications of the theory. But it would be unwise to discard a theory for which there is an abundance of evidence merely because a few facets are not understood.

THE ACTION OF MUTATIONS

It is interesting to speculate on how mutations actually produce the symptoms that are recognized as senescence. It is certainly clear that each cell type has a different function to perform, and there are a vast number of different ways in which a cell can mutate. Thus there is a double complexity to the problem and it is small wonder it is difficult to grasp. However, certain generalities seem reasonable. First, one of the prominent features of aging is cancer induction. The mutations hypothesis of carcinogenesis is too well known to repeat here, and the more that is learned about it the more probable it seems that at least one phase of the process, the induction phase, is caused by some kind of mutation (Curtis 1965). The promotion phase is not. Thus if the promotion phase is the limiting one for a particular tumor, then an inducer would not be expected to increase the frequency. Thus the fact that a few tumors have been found whose appearance is not hastened by radiation is not surprising.

A lethal mutation is one of the most likely forms to be induced either spontaneously or by a mutagen. In a mammal, if a lethal mutation occurs in the bone marrow, for example, that cell dies and its place is quickly taken by an intact cell. But if it takes place in an organ whose cells cannot divide, like the brain, then cells with lethal mutations will die and not be replaced. It is well recognized by now that cell loss in such organs is an accompaniment of aging and probably is responsible for many of the symptoms observed.

Many of the symptoms of aging from a pathological point of view are referable to a failing capillary circulation. The cells of the endothelial lining of the vessels undergo division occasionally. If such a cell suffered a mutation and came to division and was unable to complete it, a defect in the capillary would be formed which would block it, perhaps permanently. Thus these cells would be expected to be quite sensitive to mutation, either spontaneous or induced, and the consequences would be serious.

The autoimmune diseases have been receiving a good deal of attention recently and by far the most likely explanation for them is that they start with a mutation in a somatic cell (Walford 1962). It is very significant that Walford, Sjaarda & Anderson (1965) recently found that amyloidosis is markedly increased by radiation.

Collagen has been implicated in aging for many years and it is quite possible that its accumulation is due to the death by lethal mutation of fibroblasts. This is undoubtedly a complex story, but it indicates that the collagen theory of aging and the mutation theory are not mutually exclusive.

The rate of living theory is quite old and has a great deal to be said for it. The cause of somatic mutations is not known, but the experiments cited above comparing the aberrations in mice and dogs show that aberrations in liver cells develop about six times faster in the animal whose metabolism is about six times larger. Here again this gives a rational basis for combining the mutation and the rate of living theories.

SUMMARY

There is a good deal of evidence indicating that mutations play a dominant role in mammalian aging, and the concept correlates very well with most of the known facts of aging. Indeed there is virtually no concrete evidence which argues against the idea. However, there are many unsolved problems. The long delay between mutation and its manifestation in terms of aging must be resolved. Chromosome aberrations constitute a rather crude measure of mutations, and probably much of the difficulty in interpreting present results is referable to this. It now seems clear that a number of factors have an important bearing on the aging process, but it is not known whether they act as independent modifying agents or as agents which affect the mutation rate of somatic cells. Among these factors are diet, the rate of energy metabolism, the genetic background, and a host of environmental factors. Finally, the concept that chromosome stability is significant in aging has some important implications for the future. It does not seem at all impossible to think of altering chromosome stability. This can be done in plants, and as we learn more about the forces and factors stabilizing large molecules it should be possible to do this for animals. There is then ample justification for pushing forward in this field, and at least one possible avenue of advance seems clear.

References

Bender, M. A. and Gooch, C. P. (1962). *Radiat. Res., 16,* 44–53.

Crowley, C. and Curtis, H. J. (1963). *Proc. Nat. Acad. Sci. U.S.A., 49,* 626–628.

Curtis, H. J. (1963). *Science, 141,* 686–694.

Curtis, H. J. (1965). *Cancer Res., 25:8,* 1305–1311.

Curtis, H. J. and Crowley, C. (1963). *Radiat. Res., 19,* 337–344.

Curtis, H. J., Leith, J. and Tilley, J. (1966). *J. Geront., 21,* 268–270.

Curtis, H. J., Tilley, J. and Crowley, C. (1964). In *Biological Effects of Neutron and Proton Irradiations,* Volume II, Vienna, IAEA, p. 143–155.

Curtis, H. J., Tilley, J., Crowley, C. and Fuller, M. (1966). *J. Geront., 21,* 365–368.

Hayflick, L. (1965). *Exp. Cell. Res., 37,* 614–636.

Krohn, P. L. (1963). *Proc. Roy. Soc., B157,* 128–147.

Lindop, P. J. and Rotblat, J. (1961). *Proc. Roy. Soc., B154,* 332–349.

Stevenson, K. G. and Curtis, H. J. (1961). *Radiat. Res., 15,* 774–784.

Szilard, L. (1959). *Proc. Nat. Acad. Sci. U.S.A., 45,* 30–42.

Tannenbaum, A. and Silverstone, H. (1953). *Advances Cancer Res., 1,* 451–502.

Walford, R. L. (1962). *J. Geront., 17,* 281–285.

Walford, R. L., Sjaarda, J. R. and Anderson, R. E. (1965). *Exp. Geront, 1,* 117–125.

DISCUSSION

DR. RUBINSTEIN: What do the two strains die of?

DR. CURTIS: This is important. They die of a wide variety of different diseases. We were very careful to pick strains which do not die of any one disease, but ones which die of a whole spectrum of tumors, of nephrosclerosis, of amyloidosis.

DR. WALFORD: Does your A-strain have a very high incidence of amyloidosis as its principal disease of aging?

DR. CURTIS: I am not a pathologist, but was under the impression that this was not true. I understood that these two strains would have a better overall spectrum of causes of death than any others that we could find.

DR. WALFORD: The A-strain has been reported to have a 48% incidence of spontaneous renal amyloidosis (Thung, *Gerontologia*, 1957. *1*, 259), but you may have a particular A-strain without this characteristic. A very critical requirement is to have a short-lived strain that does indeed die of multiple random causes and not of any particular or chief cause. This is very hard to get.

DR. VOGT: Have you ever used the kidney?

DR. CURTIS: No, but we have a program looking at other organs.

DR. KROHN: The kidney would be quite unsatisfactory for use in A-strain mice because of the very high incidence of nephrosclerosis. The elderly A-strain mouse has practically no kidney left.

DR. ORGEL: Has this type of experiment been done on many strains?

DR. CURTIS: Yes.

DR. BRONOWSKI: The striking thing that you have shown is that the aberrations in the livers of the short-lived strain continue to rise to well over 60%, and really flatten out only when everyone has died. The other figures for the long-lived strain show that beyond the median age, nothing more is happening.

DR. CURTIS: I think the rate keeps on going up more or less. The error associated with these points is fairly large and as a general rule the curve is more or less of a straight line going out just as far as you care to take it.

DR. SINEX: These are animals that have particular mitotic rates and characteristic life-spans. If your hypothesis is correct then at the same adjusted life-span of the two groups the rate of chromosome aberrations should be more or less the same.

DR. MAYNARD SMITH: The animals that are alive at 700 days are a selected sample of the ones you started with. It would fit your theory nicely if these are the ones who have had fewer aberrations.

DR. DULBECCO: Do these mitoses carrying chromosome bridges last longer?

DR. CURTIS: The mitotic cycle is longer. There certainly is evidence that if a cell is damaged, it takes longer to get through the initial phases and get into the cell division phase.

DR. DULBECCO: Taking the proportion of mitoses with bridges as a measure of incidence of the chromosome aberration is valid only if the mitosis lasts for the same length of time in the two strains.

DR. CURTIS: Mitosis is delayed in a damaged cell, so this causes some error. One can see this in aberration frequency with time, indicating that initially a portion of the damaged cells did not get beyond prophase and were thus not scored. As they recovered they were able to complete the mitosis and were scored as abnormal. This means that the aberration percentage is scored somewhat too low for this reason.

DR. STERN: Are the mitotic indices the same? Do the same relative proportion of cells go into division in the different strains?

DR. CURTIS: I do not know. We give the mouse a dose of carbon tetrachloride and 72 hr later we kill it, take a smear, and look at it until 100 cells in anaphase have been seen of which so many are normal and so many abnormal. Thus the mitotic index, per se, should not influence the results.

DR. DULBECCO: Are you sure that carbon tetrachloride does not induce chromosome breaks?

DR. CURTIS: No, but we are really interested only in comparing one with another; if you prefer, one carbon tetrachloride poisoned mouse with another carbon tetrachloride poisoned mouse. We also have some preliminary data on animals which were surgically hepatectomized. The data are already good enough to conclude that there is not much, if any, difference between the responses to two very different stimuli.

DR. TILL: Do you know that the amount of carbon tetrachloride that reaches the liver is the same in both strains?

DR. CURTIS: No. But I do not see how this would influence the results since we are dealing only with ratios.

DR. SINEX: Is there any evidence that periodic hepatectomy improves liver function with age?

DR. CURTIS: Yes. There are some questionable but plausible clinical reports indicating that inhaling hydrocarbon liver poisons may improve liver function in persons suffering from liver dysfunction provided it does not kill the patient.

DR. PUCK: This high rate of chromosome aberrations in a mouse must be tissue-specific. I have never looked at the liver but slides of bone marrow and spleen do not show anything even approaching 20% of aberrations, under similar conditions.

DR. CURTIS: This is exactly the point. These other cells undergo cell division and they slough off the chromosome aberrations. So you have to choose an organ like the liver, which has a very small normal mitotic index, where chromosomal aberrations are not eliminated by cell selection.

DR. MAYNARD SMITH: I think nobody, not even Alexander, would really argue about a statement that radiation brings forward in time a number of different causes of death, some of which are not malignant at all. If, on the other hand, you say there really is some fundamental effect, in that radiation brings almost all causes of death forward by the same kind of amount, then Alexander would certainly argue with you and I think he would be right.

DR. CURTIS: I think almost all causes of death are speeded up; for example, the numbers of mice dying of leukemia is about the same, except that the leukemia is induced earlier. But the radiation does not speed up everything by the same amount. The induction of a tumor is unquestionably a complex process. There are certainly two, and probably up to five different steps, which must be taken to form a tumor. Radiation seems to alter one of the factors which is responsible for tumor induction but does not, in general, alter the others. Therefore, if you take some tumor, like the hepatoma that Alexander worked with, and if that is rate limited by something other than the part which is affected by radiation, then you would not expect the radiation to have any effect on the formation of the tumor and indeed it does not. In a very remarkable way radiation simulates the aging process but it is not perfect.

DR. SINEX: How do you explain the fact that the lag is inversely proportional to the dose?

DR. CURTIS: I do not think the dose has anything to do with the lag.

DR. BRONOWSKI: Two things struck me particularly. One was the remarkable results obtained by using fast neutrons instead of X-rays. The second was the very interesting observation that, after damage by neutrons, the liver can, as it were, rehabilitate itself when it is forced into division by giving carbon tetrachloride.

DR. ATWOOD: In many other contexts, if the frequency of aberrations versus the dose is plotted the dicentrics require two breaks and with X-rays the relationship is curved. With neutrons, however, it is perfectly linear. Furthermore, with neutrons, the dose rate usually makes no difference, whereas, with X-rays the dose rate makes a difference, provided it is low enough. The implication is that there must be two breaks and, if the dose rate is not high, there is time to repair one of them before the other is induced. So only a residuum remains of the aberrations that happen to form within a given repair time and this is proportional to dose at the low dose rates. On the other hand, with the neutrons, mysterious though it may seem, every time the neutron makes one break, it appears to make another one. Now the odd thing about the effect of neutrons in Dr. Curtis' experiments is that no spontaneous cleansing of the liver occurred. Carbon tetrachloride had to be given or hepatectomy performed. Yet, with gamma-rays, there is a spontaneous decrease so that one has to explain this by something else besides cell selection. I wonder what that other thing could be?

DR. CURTIS: What it is I, too, do not know, but the amazing thing is that this repair process goes on in a cell for months if it does not have to divide.

DR. ORGEL: You say there must be two events in a single cell. Is there some necessary coupling between them that has got something to do with, let us say, the structure of the chromosome?

DR. ATWOOD: I believe so. The necessary assumption which has some experimental backing of a rather indirect kind, is that in a cell the chromosome strands are arranged in such a way that only in a few places are they close enough together to rejoin to form an aberration. The implication is that the rejoining distance is small enough to be inside of the radius of influence of the projected densely ionizing particle, whatever this may be.

DR. BRANDES: I would like to make some comments about the cytoplasmic changes which occur after radiation and also after the use of alkylating agents and which should not be forgotten when we concentrate on the nucleus. Acid hydrolytic enzymes increase after irradiation. This has been shown biochemically in normal tissues and electron microscopy also shows that there is first an increase of lysosomes. Within a short period of time, possibly 2 or 3 days, the lysosomes release the enzymes and begin a process of focal degradation in the cytoplasm. These lysosomes contain approximately 15 or 16 enzymes, among them RNA-ase and DNA-ase. Some of the DNA-ase possibly may penetrate into the nucleus and affect the DNA there. Furthermore, carbon tetrachloride may have increased and provoked the release of some of the lysosomal enzymes in the liver.

DR. BRONOWSKI: I am rather worried by the unevenness of the data presented to justify the conclusion that the differing life-spans of mice and dogs are clearly reflected in differences in the rate of accumulation of chromosomal aberrations. The conclusion for mice is based on measurements from a very large number of animals, but for dogs it rests inevitably on evidence from very few animals indeed. Any relationship between age and proportions of aberrations in the livers of dogs is, therefore, much more uncertain and can only be compared very cautiously with the situation in mice.

DR. CURTIS: You are, of course, quite correct in pointing out that the accuracy of the observations on mice is a great deal better than for dogs. However, these results have been subjected to rigorous statistical analysis which indicates that the conclusions drawn are valid. Any further conclusions from these data on dogs should be reached only after equally rigorous statistical analysis, since we terminated this experiment as soon as we had enough data to prove our point.

DR. SINEX: Dr. Curtis has presented a very important series of experiments. Some things, however, are not entirely consistent with the interpretation that chromosomal aberrations are really the cause of aging. I do believe that ionizing radiation simulates certain aspects of aging mechanisms, but there may be other ways in which this is brought about. First, the dose required, particularly of neutrons, to increase chromosomal aberrations is relatively small compared to the doses required to give a significant effect on life shortening. Then the expression of aging occurs sometime after the aberrations have disappeared. There is the problem of why the incidence of chromosomal aberrations in the short- and long-lived populations is not the same when the rate of dying is the same. There are also technical problems such as whether the incidence or the duration of abnormal mitoses is being measured and the question as to whether the response to carbon tetrachloride differs in young and old animals. My own feeling is that ionizing radiation may affect an induction process—which starts aging.

DR. CURTIS: Some very recent data of ours bring out the difficulties. We took another pair of strains of mice, the 129 strain, a very long-lived strain, and the C58 which dies with a median life-span of about 10 months, specifically from leukemia. It was developed from a long-lived strain by a mutant which induces leukemia at a relatively early age. There is no difference in the rate at which chromosome aberrations accumulate in the two strains in spite of the fact that one has a median life-span of about 30 months and the other of about 10 months.

Dr. Sinex also mentioned the long lag period between the time when mutation occurs in the cell and its expression in terms of the shortening of the life-span of the animal. It would be easy to say that one has damaged DNA but that the cells, being highly differentiated, do not need DNA any more and continue on RNA. However, the turnover rate for RNA in mammalian and other kinds of cells is much too fast for this sort of argument to succeed.

It would be convenient if one could say that as soon as an animal develops 55% aberrations it will die. Unfortunately, it just is not true. Furthermore, it is very much a function of when the aberrations are produced. Reverting to Szilard's concept that faults develop in the homologous part of two chromosomes and determine the life-span, that must also be incorrect, as Dr. Kohn pointed out, because radiation given late in the life of a mouse does not affect the life-span at all, whereas one might have expected radiations given in later life to be more and not less effective.

DR. SINEX: Jack Buchanan now has definitely shown a finite life for a messenger RNA in bacteria and a relatively long life at that, and furthermore he believes that the finite life is in turn controlled by some sort of operator gene [Guthrie, G. D. & Buchanan, J. M. (1966). *Fed. Proc. 25* 864–873].

DR. DULBECCO: The life of the messenger is completely irrelevant here because when the DNA chain, with a million genes, is damaged the gene which is important for function is probably never going to be hit because the cross section is so small, and will always survive. Functionally, the formation of chromosomal aberrations may be completely irrelevant; the message will be made and everything may function perfectly normally, as long as the cell does not have to replicate its own DNA.

DR. SALLMAN: But how do you answer the other question? Why does it affect the short-lived strain?

DR. DULBECCO: It could be a different phenomenon because I do not think radiation only damages the DNA. Radiation does a lot of other things as well.

DR. KOHN: One of them is pericapillary fibrosis which is scarcely ever mentioned and, as I pointed out yesterday, is a very consistent finding in the late effects of radiation (Casarett, G. W., in *Cellular Basis and Aetiology of Late Somatic Effects of Ionizing Radiation,* 1963. R. J. C. Harris, Ed., Academic Press, New York). This could very well explain the delay and be a completely independent agent of aging.

DR. PUCK: I would like to add a word of caution against drawing conclusions about the effects of radiation on the whole body from the responses of very slowly dividing tissues. Rapidly turning over tissues like bone marrow may behave very differently. A dose of even 200 rads depletes the bone marrow to about 5% of its initial number of nucleated cells. The survivors which must undoubtedly include many kinds of mutational changes will then repopulate virtually the whole tissue.

DR. TILL: In considering the different effects of neutrons and X-rays on the number of aberrations, one ought to take into account the relative biological efficiency of neutrons versus X-rays and the fact that this varies according to the system one is looking at. How, too, is one to explain these aberrations which keep showing up at very late dates? A similar puzzle is presented by cells in peripheral blood where the aberrations in man may show up years after irradiation.

DR. CURTIS: You may have noticed on some of the slides an increase for a period even up to 90 days. I have interpreted this as being that, at first, the damaged cells are not able to undergo division and therefore they are not scored, whereas after 2 or 3 months the cells recover enough to go into division and will then be scored as aberrations. This is a fairly constant finding with X-rays, although not always, but it is never seen with neutrons.

DR. WILLIAMS: Do I understand that almost none of the animals died of liver disease?

DR. CURTIS: Yes.

DR. WILLIAMS: Nevertheless, you are saying that what is happening in the liver is representative of what is happening everywhere else.

DR. CURTIS: Yes.

DR. PUCK: One can be sure that it does not happen everywhere else. For one thing the number of bone marrow anomalies observed at various times is very different. And second, cell depletion in the liver after radiation is extremely small, whereas after 200 rads, 95% of the nucleated cell population of the bone marrow is depleted within 48 hr.

DR. CURTIS: The experiments in which the liver was caused to undergo division repeatedly showed the same sequence you have just described for bone marrow. Thus liver can be made to rather closely simulate the other kinds of cells in the mammal, but the simulation is not, of course, perfect.

DR. HASTINGS: Does everybody here visualize exactly the same thing when referring to a chromosome break or a chromosome aberration? I know from the experience of others on slow-neutron radiation of such simple things as cysteine, ATP, and insulin that many things happen. So could somebody tell us what, at the molecular level, chromosomal aberration is?

DR. ATWOOD: You wanted to know whether there would be general agreement about the molecular nature of the chromosome break. Today the answer is no, but I would say that within about 2 years from now it will become obvious. There are certain issues involved, such as whether the chromosome is multi-stranded or has only one or two strands and whether there are any non-DNA linkers interspersed in the chromosome. The weight of evidence today is in favor of very few strands and no protein linkers. One could conceive of a break of the backbone of the DNA chain.

The rejoining process is not well understood. Presumably one chain end has to be activated with a triphosphate, but first the ends would have to be revised so that they present proper nucleotide and nucleoside ends rather than some randomly broken positions in the backbone. That would require nucleases to trim the ends, and repair enzymes to close the gaps.

DR. WALFORD: In speaking of somatic mutation, one tends to think only of mutations which are intrinsically deleterious to the cell. One can, however, visualize many kinds of somatic mutation which are not intrinsically deleterious at all, for example, a mutation from an Rh positive to an Rh negative cell would have no influence on the cell's metabolism. There are large numbers of analogous antigenic factors on all cells. Cells carrying such mutations would not be eliminated merely by cell division. They could be eliminated by interaction between populations of cells, not by intracellular mechanisms, for they are really "normal" cells. It may be that this kind of mutation is involved in the rapidly dividing cell population mentioned by Dr. Puck.

It is of interest to me that when you are dealing with an animal which has only post-mitotic cells, such as adult insects, the amount of irradiation required to induce life shortening is more or less on a level with that which you said will damage the central nervous system of higher animals. This system is also composed of post-mitotic cells. But when you are dealing with an animal with many dividing cell populations such as mammals, then a far smaller amount of irradiation is needed to shorten life-span.

CELL CULTURE AND THE AGING PHENOMENON*†

Leonard Hayflick

Wistar Institute of Anatomy and Biology,
Philadelphia, Pennsylvania

The thesis that vertebrate aging is most probably a phenomenon resulting from events at the supracellular level has often been concluded from experiments purporting to show that isolated vertebrate cells are capable of indefinite multiplication when grown *in vitro* (Pearl 1922; Bidder 1925; Cowdry 1952; Medawar 1958; Maynard Smith 1962; Muller 1963; Comfort 1964). The notion that isolated animal cells in culture are capable of unlimited proliferation has profoundly influenced thinking on many fundamental biological questions, not the least of which are theories of senescence. It will be my purpose to re-examine the evidence for the view that cells grown *in vitro* are capable of indefinite multiplication and to challenge the common interpretation of those results.

It is Alexis Carrel to whom credit is given for first observing that animal cells released from *in vivo* control mechanisms by *in vitro* cultivation perpetuate themselves indefinitely. This so-called "immortality" of cultured cells was based on a series of experiments designed to show that fibroblasts derived from the heart of a chick embryo could be kept in an active state of division for an indeterminate period of time (Ebeling 1913; Parker 1961). Since, even with more modern and sophisticated cell culture techniques, actively dividing chick cells cannot be maintained much beyond 1 year, there is serious doubt that this common interpretation of Carrel's experiment is valid. An alternative explanation lies in the method of chick embryo extract preparation used as a source of nutrients for Carrel's cultures. This material was prepared daily under conditions that easily permitted cell survival and thereby contributed new, viable, embryonic cells to the chick heart strain at each feeding. Waves of

* These studies were supported (in part) by United States Public Health Service Career Development Award 5-K3-CA-5938 and Contract PH-43-62-157 from the National Cancer Institute.

† The Discussion for this article will be found on p. 117 following the paper by Puck et al.

mitotic activity were reported to be coincidental with the periodic addition of chick embryo extract (Ebeling 1913). The chick embryo pernaps has been the most popular source of cells for tissue cultures, yet no one has succeeded in confirming Carrel's studies. Nevertheless, Carrel's conclusion that isolated vertebrate cells are capable of indefinite multiplication is correct—but for the wrong reasons.

It is now known that normal or cancerous cells derived from almost all vertebrate (and some insect) tissue can be cultivated *in vitro* for various periods of time. Such cell populations divide for a finite number of generations, and after cessation of mitotic activity finally undergo total degeneration. These events may span a period of days, weeks, or months but do not exceed 1 or 2 years. Cell populations first released from tissue by enzymatic or mechanical means and cultivated *in vitro* are usually called "primary cultures" (Figure 1, Phase I). If such a population is capable of further cell division, thus necessitating transfer to more culture vessels (Figure 1, Phase II), the result is a serially passaged cell culture, which we have chosen to call a "cell strain" (Hayflick & Moorhead 1961). Multiplication in long-term culture is less likely to occur in fixed post-mitotic or highly differentiated parenchymal cells; consequently, the kind of cell population most likely to divide for long periods of time *in vitro* consists of fibroblasts, regardless of the tissue of origin. The ultimate cessation of cell division is followed by complete degeneration of the strain and is designated Phase III (Figure 1).

Cell strains have at least three fundamental properties:

1. When derived from normal tissue, they possess the morphologic, physiologic, and immunologic properties of normal cells during their *in vitro* life. When cell strains are derived from tumor tissue, they retain those properties.

2. They have the karyotype of the cells of the tissue of origin. For example, when derived from normal human tissue, cell strains have the diploid number of 46 chromosomes and display the classic human karyotype. Female cells retain sex chromatin at interphase.

3. Cell strains have limited potential for multiplication *in vitro* and undergo a finite number of cell doublings.

Thus, the establishment of a cell strain is the most common consequence of animal tissue first cultivated *in vitro*. It is our contention that the regularly repopulated cell cultures of Carrel were of this type. Subsequently, Gey & Gey (1936) and Earle (1943) demonstrated the spontaneous occurrence in cell culture of murine cells, unequivocally, capable of dividing for an indeterminate period of time.

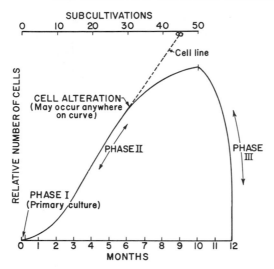

Fig. 1. Diagrammatic representation of the theory of *in vitro* vertebrate cell proliferation. Phase I, or the primary culture, terminates with the formation of the first confluent cell sheet. Phase II is characterized by more cell multiplication necessitating repeated subcultivations. Cells in Phases II and III are termed "cell strains." Cell strains characteristically enter Phase III and are lost after a finite period of time. Conversely, a spontaneous alteration could occur at any point on the curve, giving rise to a "cell line" whose potential for further multiplication is infinite. However, thus far human diploid fibroblast strains have not been found to alter spontaneously. The abscissa indicates the number of cell passages (doublings) expected from human diploid cell strains of embryonic origin and, although the shape of the curve is identical for all cell strains, the passage numbers may vary.

Since then, well over 225 cell populations with the extraordinary capacity to multiply indefinitely *in vitro* have been spontaneously derived from primary cultures or derived from cell strains of various kinds of mammalian tissue (Hayflick & Moorhead 1962). These cell populations, previously designated "cell lines" (Hayflick & Moorhead 1961), are morphologically distinguishable from cell strain populations (Hayflick 1961). The biologic characteristics of cell lines led us to conclude that regardless of the tissue of origin, whether normal or cancerous, all such populations were composed of abnormal cells and often shared properties with cancer cells.

Thus, *cell lines* have at least three fundamental properties:

1. When inoculated into suitable hosts, the cells often multiply and sometimes metastasize. Cells from human cell lines inoculated into terminal cancer patients behave in this fashion (Southam, Moore

& Rhoads 1957). Most cell lines grow when placed in the immuno-logically privileged site of the hamster cheek pouch (Handler & Foley 1956; Foley & Handler 1957, 1958). Diploid cell strains will not multiply long in either environment (Hayflick & Moorhead 1961).

2. They do not have the karyotype of the tissue (or strain) of origin and are usually heteroploid, aneuploid or, rarely, psuedo-diploid. Most often they exhibit a distribution of chromosome num-bers around a modal value which in the case of human cell lines is usually in the seventies. Sex chromatin is not retained in cell lines derived from female tissue.

3. Cell lines will, apparently, multiply indefinitely *in vitro*. Some have been in continuous cultivation in many laboratories 20 years or longer and have a doubling time of 24 hr.

Cell lines bear a relationship to cell strains that may be similar to the relationship of transplantable tumors to normal tissue. Cell strains and cell lines may be the *in vitro* counterparts of, respectively, normal cells and cancer cells *in vivo*. We can consider this relation-ship to be:

Cell Lines : Transplantable Tumors = Cell Strains : Somatic Cells

(*in vitro*) (*in vivo*)	(*in vitro*) (*in vivo*)
1. Heteroploid	1. Diploid
2. Cancer cells (histologic criteria)	2. Normal Cells
3. Indefinite potential for division	3. Finite potential for division

Thus, the phenomenon of the alteration of a cell strain to a cell line is important because, in its simplest terms, it may be regarded as oncogenesis *in vitro*. Until recently, when cell lines were obtained from fish tissue (Wolf & Quimby 1962), no nonmammalian cell lines had been authenticated. The spontaneous occurrence of a cell line is a rare event in the cultivation of most animal cell strains. The major exception to this generalization has been the behavior of mouse cells which, when cultured *in vitro*, have the unique property of almost always spontaneously altering from a cell strain to a cell line with the concomitant acquisition of the ability to multiply indefinitely (Rothfels, Kupelwieser & Parker 1963; Todaro & Green 1963).

After Carrel's studies, much of the early work in tissue culture was done with murine cells and it was reasonable to extrapolate the ob-servations made with chick and murine cells and to conclude that all animal cells cultivated *in vitro* would, under the proper condi-tions, divide indefinitely. We contend that this generalization, without a critical qualification, is fallacious and that the normal somatic cells of these two species behave diametrically opposite when cultivated *in vitro*. Confirmation of reported chick cell lines has never been substantiated, yet most mouse cell strains eventually alter to a cell line population. The essential qualification to the generalization lies in the fact that only cells acquiring malignant or abnormal properties *in vitro* are capable of unlimited division. The *in vitro* behavior of normal vertebrate somatic cells, which is pivotal to the development of many theories of vertebrate aging, reveals that they *do* have a finite lifetime.

There is reason to believe that, even with the limited evidence available, a graded scale might be imagined representing the predisposition for alteration to a cell line by the cells of various animal species. Chick cells would lie at the base of the scale and mouse cells at the top, with human cells positioned somewhere near the base. An explanation for these relationships is not known, although it is intriguing to observe that old laboratory mice of the strains usually used for tissue culture almost always die of cancer (Strong 1935) and mouse cells when grown *in vitro* often acquire such properties.

It is important to stress that alterations occur fortuitously in cell cultures and under conditions that, until recently, could not be defined. The spontaneous alterations described in the literature (Hayflick & Moorhead 1962) have emerged in many different kinds of culture environments. Conditions for reproducibly altering cell strains to cell lines, if known, would be a powerful tool for the study of the *in vitro* conversion of normal cells (strains) to cancer or abnormal cells (lines). Recently, it was discovered that the infection of human diploid cell strains with the virus S.V.$_{40}$ (Koprowski, Pontén, Jensen, Ravdin, Moorhead & Saksela 1962; Shein & Enders 1962) and diploid rodent strains infected with polyoma virus could provide these conditions (Vogt & Dulbecco 1960; Sachs & Medina 1961).

However, of interest to us presently is that characteristic of cell strains in which they are capable of only a limited number of doublings *in vitro* and what relevance this observation may have to our understanding of senescence phenomena. It should now be clear that since heteroploid cell lines share properties with cancer or abnormal cells, considerations of aging at the cellular level must be related to the behavior of normal diploid cell strains *in vitro*. In fact, any theory of aging must have as a corollary an explanation for the apparent escape from senescence by malignant cells both *in vitro* and *in vivo*.

On this basis, arguments marshalled against cellular theories of aging must be reevaluated if they are based on the myth of "immortal" cell cultures, because the cells that proliferate indefinitely *in vitro* are abnormal and usually behave like cancer cells. Contrariwise, normal cells *in vitro* have a finite life-span as do the animals from which such cells have been taken. There is no confirmed evidence that normal cells can be maintained in a state of active proliferation in cell culture for a period of time in excess of the specific age of the species from which the cells were obtained. It is our contention that *in vivo* vertebrate senescence phenomena at the level of the cell also occurs *in vitro* when the proper systems are compared.

In earlier work with human embryonic diploid cell strains derived from lung tissue, we observed that after a period of active multiplication, generally less than 1 year, these cells demonstrated an increased doubling time (normally 24 hr), gradual cessation of mitotic activity, accumulation of cellular debris and, ultimately, total degeneration of the culture. This phenomenon, called Phase III (Figure 1), has been a common observation by cell culturists who used cells from many types of tissue. In the past, technical difficulties have usually been invoked to explain this event. We view this phenomenon as an innate characteristic of all normal cells grown *in vitro* and believe that optimum conditions for the multiplication of mammalian cells do exist. The Phase III phenomenon in the course of the *in vitro* cultivation of human diploid cell strains derived from fetal lung tissue occurs after about 50 cell doublings (Hayflick 1965). Diploid strains derived from other organs give essentially similar results. This event, now confirmed in many laboratories, is unrelated to media composition, presence of microorganisms, or the depletion of some nonreplicating metabolic pool. Consequently, it has been hypothesized that the finite lifetime of diploid cell strains *in vitro* may be the cellular manifestation of aging that is well known at the level of the whole animal (Hayflick & Moorhead 1961; Hayflick 1965).

Since diploid cell strains have a limited doubling potential *in vitro,* studies on any single strain would be severely limited were it not possible to preserve these cells at subzero temperatures for apparently indefinite periods of time. This maneuver allows for the construction of a number of interesting experiments. The reconstitution of frozen human fetal diploid cell strains has revealed that regardless of the doubling level reached by the population at the time it is preserved, the *total* number of doublings than can be expected is about 50, including those made prior to and after preservation (Hayflick & Moorhead 1961; Hayflick 1965). Storage of human diploid cell strains merely arrests the cells at a particular doubling level but does not influence the total number of expected doublings. We have also shown that the ability to double 50 times is probably a characteristic of each clonable cell in the population and that mixed populations of cells with different doubling potentials do not influence each other.

Of greater importance, perhaps, is the finding that diploid cell strains derived from the lungs of *adult* humans reach Phase III after about 20 doublings *in vitro* (Hayflick 1965). Although cell strains from a number of young and old adults were studied, no precise correlation was found between the number of doublings *in vitro* and the chronological age of the donor. If such a correlation does exist, present methods of determining number of doublings are too imperfect to uncover the relationship. Nevertheless, it is clear that the doubling potential of embryonic human diploid cell strains is far greater than that of cell strains derived from adults.

Human diploid fibroblast strains derived from adult tissue are, with the exception of doubling potential, biologically identical to those derived from embryos. Adult strains preserved at low temperatures can also be arrested at any doubling level, yet the total number of doublings possible is about 20. We have postulated a mechanism to explain these phenomena that depends upon an accumulation of a greater burden of heritable damage by adult cells before cultivation *in vitro* than by embryonic cells (Hayflick 1965). The shape of the curve obtained by plotting the numbers of cells produced per unit period of time throughout the finite lifetime of a human diploid cell population is similar to a multiple-hit or multiple-target curve. It appears that some critical level which affects a vulnerable cellular target(s), must be reached before exponential death of the cell population results. Since 50 doublings preclude any simple dilution or accumulation phenomenon, the effect is upon some selfduplicating cellular system and consequently must be heritable. It is conceivable that DNA copying errors result in the ultimate inability of the cell to properly program itself, after 50 doublings, for the next division. The precision of this event is understandable in terms of the mean time to failure in the operation of any group of complex machines whose repair systems are imperfect. Alternatively, it is possible that some self-duplicating entity essential for cell division is, itself, dividing at a rate somewhat slower than that of the cells. Conditions could be envisioned wherein such a process would ultimately result in the complete loss of this essential entity after 50 doublings with the concomitant inability of the cell itself to divide. This is somewhat analogous to the Kappa factor relationships occurring in some strains of paramecium (Sonneborn 1959).

If the concept that the finite lifetime of normal cells *in vitro* is related to a potential finite lifetime of cells *in situ,* then it would be valuable to answer the question: Can normal somatic cells divide indefinitely under any conditions? Certainly, the best conditions would be those offered by an *in vivo* environment, and the question could be answered by serial orthotopic transplantation of normal somatic tissue to new, young, inbred hosts each time the recipient approaches old age. Under these conditions, do transplanted normal cells of age-chimeras proliferate indefinitely? Data from a number of laboratories suggest that normal cells, serially transplanted to inbred hosts, apparently do not survive indefinitely. In the studies of DeOme (1965), normal mammary tissue from adult mice were transplanted into a group of 3-week-old (virgin) mice of the same inbred strain who, when 5-months-old, served as donors for the next transplant generation. This process was repeated for 40 to 45 months when the outgrowths could not be found and, therefore, could not be further transplanted. Similar results were obtained with three different strains of mice. Serial transplantation experiments employing hyperplastic alveolar tissue rather than normal mammary tissue yielded quite different results. Three such tissues were serially transplanted for more than 5 years and showed no diminution in growth rate.

The proliferative ability of transplanted normal hematopoietic cells also has been found to be finite. In the studies of Ford, Micklem & Gray (1959), proliferating hematopoietic cells, identifiable by means of a chromosome marker, were unable to repopulate the organs of heavily irradiated recipient mice after the third transplant generation. Systematic studies of the eventual loss of proliferative ability of marrow cells after serial transplantation have also been reported by others (Cudkowicz, Upton, Shearer & Hughes 1964). In recent studies, this point has been well amplified. Using cells derived from normal fetal mouse liver (Till, McCulloch & Siminovitch 1964), and from spleen or marrow (Siminovitch, Till & McCulloch 1964), it has been shown that, with repeated passage in irradiated hosts, such cells eventually lose their ability to form colonies in the spleen. This phenomenon, termed "decline," is interpreted as indicating that new colony-forming cells are not identical with their progenitors since they differ in their capacity for self-renewal. Furthermore, these investigators conclude that the "loss of colony-forming ability with repeated passage suggests that the proliferative capacity of normal hematopoietic colony-forming cells, though extensive, is not unlimited." Incidentally, the loss of colony-forming or proliferative ability with repeated transplantation parallels loss of the ability of these cells to prevent the death of supralethally irradiated animals. The antithesis of these results is obtained when leukemic cells are used since these cells retain their proliferative capacity through apparently indefinite numbers of successive transplantations (Bruce & Meeker 1964). Of interest in this regard is the further observation of Till, McCulloch & Siminovitch (1964) that in those few cases where transplanted mouse liver cells showed no decrease in proliferative capacity, they were found to differ from normal hematopoietic cells and to behave like lymphoma cells.

In the series of mouse skin transplantation experiments devised by Krohn (1962), this initial report suggested that grafts from young donors remained in satisfactory condition for about 650 to 1000 days and after two to five transplantations. However, the grafts began to decrease in size at that time, and between 850 and 1750 days the transplants had become "minute areas of skin which were unsuitable for further transplantation." In comparison with the longest recorded life-span of 3½ years for any mouse (Roberts 1961), the maximum life-span of skin transplants ranged from 4½ to 5 years. One might conclude that transplanted normal mouse tissue does not exhibit the kind of indefinite proliferative capacities characteristic of transplantable mouse tumors, some of which have been passaged for decades *in vivo* (Stewart, Snell, Dunham & Schlyen 1959). More recently, however, Krohn (1966) has reported that some mouse skin transplants are surviving for periods of time in excess of those originally reported and, perhaps, may not exhibit a diminution in transplantability. In such cases, it would be valuable to determine whether during these long periods of time, cell proliferation is continuing in the grafts or whether serial transfer merely represents maintenance of vegetative cells. If not, it would be important to determine whether, in fact, the cells composing the grafts were still karyotypically normal. It is possible that abnormal cell populations may sometimes result from serial transplantations similar to the occurrence of spontaneous alterations in populations of normal cells serially subcultivated *in vitro*. A report of just such a finding has been detailed above in the studies of transplanted normal mouse liver cells in which a few populations of apparently indefinitely transplantable cell types emerged and were later found to behave like lymphoma cells (Till, McCulloch & Siminovitch, 1964).

One implication of the foregoing observations may be that acquisition of potential for unlimited cell division or escape from senescent changes by mammalian somatic cells *in vitro* or *in vivo* can only be achieved by cells that behave abnormally or, perhaps, as cancer cells. Paradoxically, this leads to the conclusion that in order for mammalian somatic cells to become biologically "immortal," they first must be induced to the neoplastic state either *in vivo* or *in vitro;* at which time they can then be subcultivated or transplanted indefinitely.

Although the karyotype of human diploid cell strains is very stable during periods of active proliferation (Phases I and II) aneuploidy and other chromosome aberrations do occur during Phase III. In this connection, a relationship has been demonstrated between chromosome aberrations of somatic cells *in vivo* and natural aging by scoring anaphase anomalies in regenerating mouse liver tissue (Crowley & Curtis 1963). Within each strain of mouse tested there was an age-correlated increase in anaphase and telophase aberrations scored following partial hepatectomy. Of even greater interest are the observations made in man that increased hypodiploid counts in the peripheral blood leucocytes are correlated with the chronological age of the donor (Jacobs, Court Brown & Doll 1961; Hamerton, Taylor, Angell & McGuire 1965). There exists, therefore, *in vivo* evidence for age-associated chromosomal anomalies that are also involved at the time of decreased proliferation of human diploid cells *in vitro* (Phase III).

Appreciation of the finite doubling potential of *normal* cells *in vitro* has launched studies to compare the specific age of a vertebrate species and the number of cell doublings accrued by their cells when grown *in vitro*. In a general way, there seems to be some relationship, since there is little doubt that the fibroblasts of man, the longest-lived mammal, undergo more doublings than do cell strains of a number of laboratory animals. It may be found that the differences in specific age of different vertebrate species may be reflected by the numbers of doublings of their unaltered normal cells when cultured *in vitro*.

The very low doubling potential of unaltered parenchymal cells *in vitro* is not an argument against the hypothesis that fibroblasts which undergo many more doublings *in vitro* may eventually age. Highly differentiated normal parenchymal cells which have a limited capacity to divide *in vivo* should not be expected to behave differently *in vitro*. Likewise those theories of aging that emphasize the critical importance of events occurring in nondividing parenchymal cells are not in jeopardy as a result of acceptance of evidence that normal cells capable of proliferating have a finite division potential. Justification for attributing senescence or other complex biological phenomena to a single causative event is probably unwarranted. It is wise to assume that in those animals where vigor declines with age, the responsible processes are multiple and to treat senescence as a sum of all these factors, one of which may be the limited number of doublings through which any normal cell can go. It is also probable that at the cellular level different events lead to the aging of different cell types. Thus the life-span of all fixed post-mitotic mammalian parenchymal cells may be limited as a result of the same kind of "copying errors" that may lead to the ultimate demise of rapidly dividing cells but which in this case may lead to reduced molecular turnover and consequent impaired cell function. Nondividing cells are also assumed to be programmed by a vulnerable DNA. The nuclei of fixed post-mitotic, nondividing parenchymal cells are surely no less susceptible to damage than those of the stem cells of proliferating tissue.

One possible reason why the finite lifetime of normal cell populations *in vitro* may not apply to cells *in vivo* is the consideration that normal bone marrow, intestinal epithelium, and basement layer cells of the skin apparently divide at the same rate until the death of the whole animal. Closer scrutiny of the mathematical concepts implicit in such conclusions reveal several alternate explanations. As delineated by Kay (1965), one extreme of cell multiplication may be envisioned as tangential (or maintenance) in which a pool of homogeneous stem cells multiplies in such a way that one daughter cell of each division becomes differentiated or functional and the other retains its stem cell characteristic, thus maintaining the size of the original pool. In this manner even though the pool size remains constant, cell division replaces only the cast-off differentiated cells, for example of the hematopoietic system or from the crypts of Lieberkuhn. The other extreme situation of cell multiplication occurs if all mitoses are synchronous and cell division is logarithmic. In this situation no stem cells would survive, and all of the differentiated cells would be produced simultaneously. However, Kay (1965) suggests that a constant supply of differentiated cells could be obtained by asynchronous division within the logarithmic model. The critical assumption is that there is a variation in the rate of division of the primitive stem cell pool that provides for the regular release of differentiated cells. Kay (1965) gives to this concept the name "clonal succession" where, in comparison with tangential division, there is a reduction in the number of cell generations necessary to produce a given population of differentiated cells. Clonal succession also allows for a closer adherence to the original hereditary blueprint. This model of asynchronous logarithmic multiplication would contain many populations of dormant ancestral cells at various doubling levels. The rate of promotion to subsequent doubling levels would depend upon a whole succession of environmental controls. An example cited by Kay (1965) is the intestinal crypts of man, where a high rate of mitosis implies a large number of cell generations. This cell turnover has been estimated to cycle at a frequency of once each 100 hr (Shorter, Moertel, Titus & Reitemeier 1964), so that the cells in the crypt bases may be undergoing 5000 mitoses in 60 years. A source of primitive stem cells must be sought if the operative mechanism is clonal succession. Such a population of slowly reproducing cells within the crypts has been described (Shorter, Moertel, Titus & Reitemeier 1964; McDonald, Trier & Everett 1964). Thus the concept of clonal succession may explain the apparent greater number of doublings of normal cells *in vivo* than occur *in vitro*, since it is clear that the entire population of cells shed by organs such as the intestine can be achieved by a stem cell population programmed for only 50, or less, divisions. Cells in culture, released from homeostatic controls, may divide more nearly like the synchronous logarithmic model, thus providing us with the evidence that normal cells are incapable of perpetuating themselves indefinitely.

The concept that normal dividing cells never have an opportunity to age because they periodically yield new daughter cells before age changes take place also bears re-examination. The question here is whether or not the product of a cell division is always a pair of daughter cells, each having the same age status. This notion makes the very important assumption that dividing cells yield daughters that are "separate but equal." There is little, if any, evidence that bears on this important point in mammalian cells, and there are no factual data opposing the possibility that one daughter cell receives one or more old organelles, while the other receives only new organelles. To assume that each daughter mammalian cell is equivalent in age status may be untrue, and cell culture may lead to an examination of this question.

Since populations of vertebrate cells in culture have an independent existence and can be manipulated like micro-organisms, it may be useful to compare certain aspects of the behavior of both. Studies with protozoa do not unequivocally demonstrate the "immortality" of unicellular organisms or that the outcome of a protozoan cell division is a pair of rejuvenated infant cells instead of a mother and daughter cell of different seniorities.

For example, it has been shown (Danielli & Muggleton 1959) that amoebae will multiply indefinitely if kept on a food supply permitting logarithmic vegetative multiplication but, if kept on a limited food supply then transferred to the optimum diet, they have a variable life-span. This span of from 30 days to 30 weeks is dependent upon the conditions of exposure to the deficient diet. Since it is likely that amoeba in the natural state do not always have an optimum food supply, their usual fate is probably one in which senescence occurs. A number of other investigators have also concluded that many clones of protozoa do not propagate asexually for an indefinite period. Such observations have been made with *Uroleptus* (Calkins 1919), *Paramecium* (Sonneborn 1938), and with an *Ascomycete* (Rizet 1953). Other clones of protozoa apparently do reproduce asexually and indefinitely. The extensive studies of Jennings (1945) bear directly on this question and on clonal rejuvenation by conjugation. It was found that the viability of the progeny of *Paramecium bursaria* by conjugation varies greatly even when the conjugants are young and that a high proportion of ex-conjugants normally die. The rate appears to be highest in those clones that are more closely related. Fifty-three per cent of ex-conjugants die before undergoing five cell divisions and 30% die without dividing at all. Conjugation produced nonviable clones, clones of limited survival, and some vigorous clones apparently capable of unlimited asexual reproduction. It is suggested that it is from these latter clones that laboratory cultures are normally obtained. Jennings concludes that death is not a consequence of multi-cellularity and that it occurs on a vast scale in the protozoa "from causes which are intrinsic to the organism." He claims that "most if not all clones ultimately die if they do not undergo some form of sexual reproduction. . . . Rejuvenation through sexual reproduction is a fact . . . yet conjugation produces, in addition to rejuvenated clones, vast numbers of weak, pathological or abnormal clones whose predestined fate is early death." He adds that some very vigorous clones may be produced "that may continue vegetatively for an indefinite period, without decline or death." Reference should be made to Comfort (1964), and Strehler (1962), for an exhaustive discussion of this subject.

On the basis of current evidence the finite lifetime of normal cells *in vitro* may not only be a model for aging in the whole organism, but indeed, might be the same phenomenon reduced to a lesser degree of complexity. A number of generally accepted age-associated phenomena found at the tissue or whole animal level lend themselves to re-examination at the level of the cultured cell. Quantitative studies such as those of Lefford (1964) clearly demonstrate that as age increases there is a concomitant prolongation of the latent period of fibroblast migration from chick heart explants *in vitro*. This confirms earlier studies (Carrel & Burrows 1911; Cohn & Murray 1925) demonstrating that the "growth rate" of emigrating fibroblasts from chick heart explants decreases with the age of the donor. The phenomenon has also been observed in explanted rat livers where it was concluded that the "growth capacity" is inversely proportional to the age of the animal (Glinos & Bartlett 1951). Similar observations have been made *in vivo* where the time-lag in reaching the peak mitotic rate lengthens with age (Howes & Harvey 1932). This age-associated parameter is now amenable to study with normal human cells *in vitro* not only with explants or monolayers but also at the level of the individual cell or clone.

Since collagen is produced by human diploid cells (Hayflick & Moorhead 1961), age related properties of this material obtained from embryonic and adult strains may be a useful area of inquiry. The contractility and thermal shrinkage of collagen, which varies with the age of rats (Verzár & Thoenen 1960), might be compared at Phases II and III. The current interest in the apparent age-accelerating effects of radiation may also be extended to include studies at the cell level where reduction in average life-span of animals exposed to ionizing radiation may have its parallel in cultured normal cells. Although the specific effects of sublethal doses of radiation on the time of occurrence of Phase III has not as yet been reported, studies which show a definite effect of radiation on the replication of human diploid cell strains have been made (Puck, Morkovin, Marcus & Cieciura 1957; Norris & Hood 1962).

The relatively recent resolution of two technical problems in the management of animal cell cultures should facilitate the design of a number of intriguing experiments bearing not only upon questions of the aging of individuals but of the entire species. The ability to establish normal diploid cell strains from small skin (or other tissue) biopsies of any individual plus the capacity to preserve these cells at subzero temperatures has fascinating experimental possibilities. Our experience with human diploid cell strains stored in liquid nitrogen extends over a period of only 4 years, yet after this time at $-190°C$ there is no diminution in rate of division or doubling potential. If such cell populations are found to retain these properties after a lapse of decades, then it might be concluded that if nondividing cells age, they can only do so while being functionally competent. Alternatively, if it is found that their viability or doubling potential diminishes with storage then preservation of cells at −190°C, where molecular activity is biologically negligible, may not protect them from the age-accelerating effects of, for example, radiation.

Although the experimenter would not be present to capitalize on his foresight, it would be a simple task to deposit ampules of normal human and animal cells in a well-protected capsule buried in the Antarctic with instructions for reconstitution. This might lead an investigator, generations hence, to compare, among other things, the evolutionary aspects of aging at the cellular level.

The purpose of this presentation is not to develop another theory of aging but merely to reconsider, in light of newer knowledge, the question of the finite lifetime of cells cultured outside the animal body and what bearing this should have on current hypotheses. It is now possible that the powerful technique of cell cultivation may be exploited in investigating problems of senescence. Once the myth of the unlimited proliferation of normal cells *in vitro* is laid to rest, more emphasis should be placed on the notion that senescence results from the greater expression of events at the cellular level than at the tissue, organ, or organism level. That is not to say that senescence, as a multi-causal phenomenon, is in no way a consequence of deteriorative supracellular events.

SUMMARY

Normal animal cells have been shown to be incapable of indefinite proliferation *in vitro*. Consequently, theories of aging, and other biological concepts, based on the immortality of the cultured normal cell bear re-evaluation. The notion that vertebrate aging is most probably a phenomenon resulting from events at the supracellular level has resulted from acceptance of the idea that cells released from *in vivo* control mechanisms by growth *in vitro* could divide indefinitely. The *in vitro* behavior of normal vertebrate somatic cells, which is pivotal to the development of theories of vertebrate aging, reveals that they *do* have a finite lifetime.

Normal human diploid embryonic fibroblasts (cell strains) undergo approximately 50 doublings *in vitro*; adult fibroblasts undergo about 20. Those cell populations capable of indefinite proliferation *in vitro* (cell lines) have abnormal properties and may behave like cancer cells. Thus, transplantable tumors are to cell lines as normal somatic tissue is to cell strains. The former populations have indefinite proliferative potential and the latter a finite lifetime.

Normal cell populations such as skin, bone marrow, and mammary tissue, serially transplanted as their hosts age, have generally been found to have a finite potential for division. Thus, an *in vivo* counterpart for the *in vitro* results are known. Similarly, chromosome anomalies that occur at the time normal human diploid cells cease to divide *in vitro* are also found to occur in the peripheral blood leucocytes of a man in direct proportion to his age.

Probable explanations for the ultimate cessation of division of normal cells *in vitro* involve multiple-hit or multiple-target phenomena. Alternatively, it is possible that some self-duplicating entity essential for cell division is, itself, dividing at a rate somewhat slower than that of the cell. Normal bone marrow, intestinal epithelium and basement layer cells of the skin apparently divide at high rates and seemingly undergo greater than 50 divisions. However, examination of the mathematical concepts implict in such a conclusion reveals that the entire complement of cells produced from these tissues during the lifetime of the animal can be encompassed by 50 or fewer cell doublings.

The very low doubling potential of unaltered parenchymal cells *in vitro* does not argue against the hypothesis that fibroblasts which undergo many more doublings *in vitro* may eventually age. Highly differentiated normal parenchymal cells that have a limited capacity to divide *in vivo* should not be expected to behave differently *in vitro*. Likewise, those theories of aging that emphasize the critical importance of events occurring in nondividing parenchymal cells are not jeopardized as a result of acceptance of evidence that normal cells capable of proliferating have a finite division potential. Justification for attributing senescence or other complex biological phenomena to a single causative event is probably unwarranted. It is wise to assume that in those animals where vigor declines with age the responsible processes are multiple and to treat senescence as a sum of all these factors, one of which may be the limited number of doublings through which any normal cell can go.

References

Bidder, G. P. (1925). *Nature, 115,* 495.
Bruce, W. R. and Meeker, B. E. (1964). *J. Nat. Cancer Inst., 32,* 1145–1159.
Calkins, G. N. (1919). *J. Exp. Zool., 29,* 121–156.
Carrel A. and Burrows, M. T. (1911). *J. Exp. Med., 13,* 562–574.

Cohn, A. E. and Murray, H. A. (1925). *J. Exp. Med., 42,* 275–290.

Comfort, A. (1964). In *Ageing: The Biology of Senescence,* Holt, Rinehart, and Winston, New York.

Cowdry, E. V. (1952). In *Cowdry's Problems of Aging,* Lansing, A. I., Ed., Williams and Wilkens, Baltimore, p. 23–49.

Crowley, C. and Curtis, H. J. (1963). *Proc. Nat. Acad. Sci., U.S.A., 49,* 626–628.

Cudkowicz, G., Upton, A. C., Shearer, G. M. and Hughes W. L. (1964). *Nature, 201,* 165–167.

Danielli, J. F. and Muggleton, A. (1959). *Gerontologia, 3,* 76–90.

DeOme, K. B. (1965). Cited in Hayflick, L., *Exp. Cell Res., 37,* 614–636.

Earle, W. R. (1943). *J. Nat. Cancer Inst., 4,* 165–212.

Ebeling, A. H. (1913). *J. Exp. Med., 17,* 273–285.

Foley, G. E. and Handler, A. H. (1957). *Proc. Soc. Exp. Biol. Med., 94,* 661–664.

Foley, G. E. and Handler, A. H. (1958). *Ann. N.Y. Acad. Sci., 76,* 506–512.

Ford, C. E., Micklem, H. S. and Gray, S. M. (1959). *Brit. J. Radiol., 32,* 280.

Gey, G. O. and Gey, M. K. (1936). *Amer. J. Cancer, 27,* 45–76.

Glinos, A. D. and Bartlett, E. G. (1951). *Cancer Res., 11,* 164–168.

Hamerton, J. L., Taylor, A. I., Angell, R. and McGuire, V. M. (1965). *Nature, 206,* 1232–1234.

Handler A. H. and Foley, G. E. (1956). *Proc. Soc. Exp. Biol. Med., 19,* 237–240.

Hayflick, L. (1961). *Exp. Cell. Res., 23,* 14–20.

Hayflick, L. (1965). *Exp. Cell Res., 37,* 614–636.

Hayflick, L. and Moorhead, P. S. (1961). *Exp. Cell Res., 25,* 585–621.

Hayflick, L. and Moorhead, P. S. (1962). In *Growth, Including Reproduction and Morphological Development,* Altman, P. L. and Dittmer, D. S., Eds., Federation of American Societies for Experimental Biology, Biological Handbook Series, Washington, D.C., p. 156–160.

Howes, E. L. and Harvey, S. C. (1932). *J. Exp. Med., 55,* 577–590.

Jacobs, P. A., Court Brown, W. M. and Doll, R. (1961). *Nature, 191,* 1178–1180.

Jenning, H. S. (1945). *J. Exp. Zool., 99,* 15–31.

Kay, H. E. M. (1965). *Lancet, ii,* 418–419.

Koprowski, H., Pontén, J. A., Jensen, F., Ravdin, R. G., Moorhead, P. S. and Saksela, E. (1962). *J. Cell Comp. Physiol., 59,* 281–286.

Krohn, P. L. (1962). *Proc. Roy. Soc., B157,* 128–147.

Krohn, P. L. (1966). This volume, p. 125.

Lefford, F. (1964). *Exp. Cell Res., 35,* 557–571.

Maynard Smith, J. (1962). *Proc. Roy. Soc., B157,* 115–127.

McDonald, W. C., Trier, J. S. and Everett, N. B. (1964). *Gastroenterology, 46,* 405–417.

Medawar, P. B. (1958). In *The Uniqueness of the Individual,* Basic Books, New York.

Muller, H. J. (1963). In *Cellular Basis and Aetiology of Late Somatic Effects of Ionizing Radiation,* Harris, R. J. C., Ed., Academic Press, New York, p. 235–245.

Norris, G. and Hood, S. L. (1962). *Exp. Cell Res., 27,* 48–62.

Parker, R. C. (1961). In *Methods of Tissue Culture,* Hoeber Medical Division, Harper and Row, New York.

Pearl, R. (1922). In *The Biology of Death,* Lippincott, Philadelphia.

Puck, T. T., Morkovin, D., Marcus, P. I. and Cieciura, S. J. (1957). *J. Exp. Med.,* *106,* 485–500.

Rizet, G. (1953). *C. R. Acad. Sci., 237,* 838–840.

Roberts, R. C. (1961). *Heredity, 16,* 369–381.

Rothfels, K. H., Kupelwieser, E. B. and Parker, R. C. (1963). In *Canadian Cancer Conference* Begg, R. W., Ed., Academic Press, New York, p. 191–223.

Sachs, L. and Medina, D. (1961). *Nature, 189,* 457–458.

Shein, H. M. and Enders, J. F. (1962). *Proc. Nat. Acad. Sci., U.S.A., 48,* 1164–1172.

Shorter, R. G., Moertel, C. G., Titus, J. L. and Reitemeier, R. J. (1964). *Am. J. Dig. Dis., 9,* 760–763.

Siminovitch, L., Till, J. E. and McCulloch, E. A. (1964). *J. Cell Comp. Physiol., 64,* 23–31.

Sonneborn, T. M. (1938). *Biol. Bull. Wood's Hole, 74,* 76–82.

Sonneborn, T. M. (1959). In *Advances in Virus Research,* Vol. 6, Smith, K. M. and Lauffer, M. A., Eds., Academic Press, New York, p. 229–356.

Southam, C. M., Moore, A. E. and Rhoads, C. P. (1957). *Science, 125,* 158–160.

Stewart, H. L., Snell, K. C., Dunham, L. J. and Schlyen, S. M. (1959). In *Transplantable and Transmissable Tumors of Animals,* Armed Forces Institute of Pathology, Washington.

Strehler, B. L. (1962). In *Time, Cells, and Aging,* Academic Press, New York.

Strong, L. C. (1935). *Genetics, 20,* 586–591.

Till, J. E., McCulloch, E. A. and Siminovitch, L. (1964). *J. Nat. Cancer Inst., 33,* 707–720.

Todaro, G. J. and Green, H. (1963). *J. Cell Biol., 17,* 299–313.

Verzár, F. and Thoenen, H. (1960). *Gerontologia, 4,* 112–119.

Vogt, M. and Dulbecco, R. (1960). *Proc. Nat. Acad. Sci. U.S.A., 46,* 365–370.

Wolf, K. and Quimby, M. C. (1962). *Science, 135,* 1065–1066.

SOME DATA BEARING ON THE LONG TERM
GROWTH OF MAMMALIAN CELLS *in vitro**[*][†]

T. T. Puck and C. A. Waldren

Eleanor Roosevelt Institute for Cancer Research and the Florence R. Sabin
  Laboratory of the Department of Biophysics,
University of Colorado Medical Center,
Denver, Colorado

J. H. Tjio

National Institutes of Health,
Bethesda, Maryland

The conceptual background dealing with the multiplication of mammalian cells *in vitro* has had a confused history, and considerable caution is still necessary in formulation of generalizations as long as logical gaps exist in the framework. The very earliest conclusions are recognized as invalid because of the presence of viable cell contaminants in the nutrient solutions used. At a later time it was believed that single mammalian cells cannot grow, multiplication being a function of a large cell population only (Fischer 1946). The group in Earle's laboratory (Sanford, Earle & Likely 1948; Earle, Bryant & Schilling 1954) first demonstrated that single mammalian cells sealed in capillaries could carry out extensive multiplication, and while these cells were of highly abnormal, heteroploid karyotype, we subsequently developed techniques whereby single cells of either normal diploid or heteroploid constitution could be simply and routinely grown into large colonies, with an efficiency and reproducibility sufficiently high to make quantitative studies possible (Puck & Marcus 1955; Puck, Marcus & Cieciura 1956; Puck, Cieciura & Fisher 1957; Puck, Cieciura & Robinson 1958). Further studies revealed that most if not all established cell cultures consist of heteroploid karyotypes (Moore, Southam & Sternberg 1956; Hsu & Moorhead 1957; Parker, Castor & McCulloch 1957). Such cultures were found

* This investigation was supported by a grant from the National Foundation.
† Contribution No. 277.

to possess the following characteristics: (*1*) The chromosomal number is highly variable even in clonal populations; (*2*) the modal chromosome number often lies in the vicinity of the triploid number for the species; (*3*) the chromosomes deviate grossly from euploidy; (*4*) an appreciable number of chromosomes with distinctly different structures from those characteristic of the normal karyotype are present. Experiments comparing the growth of freshly biopsied diploid cultures with these "established" heteroploid ones revealed that the former invariably slowed down and stopped multiplying often within 5 subcultures, or else spontaneously altered to the heteroploid form (Moore et al. 1956; Swim & Parker 1957). Hsu and Moorhead (1957), among others, postulated that only the heteroploid karyotype can multiply for long periods *in vitro*. For this reason, tissue cultures other than primary explants were considered unusable for karyotypic analysis.

Studies undertaken in our laboratory demonstrated that if environmental conditions were properly controlled much more reliable growth behavior could be obtained from diploid cells: (*1*) Cell cultures could routinely and reliably be initiated from small biopsies of a large variety of tissues of adult or embryonic animals including man. (*2*) Such cultures could be maintained in active growth for periods sometimes as great as a year or more. (*3*) These cultures also maintained a normal, diploid karyotype for a great many generations, in some cases estimated to be in the neighborhood of 100, although the exact count was not certain (Puck et al. 1958; Tjio & Puck 1958a,b). As Ford (1962) has pointed out, these methodologies applied to skin biopsies made possible the first analysis of chromosome constitution on any person, and so relieved experimenters of the limitation of being confined to fetal or testicular biopsies, and hence contributed to the rapid, early growth of the new field of chromosomal medicine (Puck & Robinson 1966). It should be noted that more recent techniques which involve only short term blood cultures are now more widely used for most routine chromosomal analysis because of their greater convenience (Moorhead, Nowell, Mellman, Battips & Hungerford 1960).

It was also noted that the epithelioid, heteroploid cells are generally far less demanding nutritionally and better able to withstand adverse environmental conditions than the diploid, fibroblast-like cells (Puck et al. 1957; Fisher, Puck & Sato 1959). Hence, these cells are likely to overgrow diploid cells in mixed cultures. Also, a number of pseudo-diploid cells, like those of the Chinese hamster, have been kept in active cultivation for many years. Here too, however (Tjio & Puck 1958a; Ham 1963a, 1965) the chromosomal number is variable and distributed about a modal number, and even clonal cultures show marked heterogeneities in chromosomal number and constitution.

Even under the carefully controlled conditions which we employed, which greatly increased the reliability and period of active multiplication of diploid cells such cultures usually eventually ceased to grow (Puck et al. 1958). The number of generations of growth which elapsed before arrest set in under these conditions was sufficiently large to make almost certain that growth cessation was not due to loss by reproductive dilution of an essential, cell-stored macromolecule not supplied in the medium. The logical question then arises: Can the generative span of diploid mammalian cells be increased significantly and perhaps indefinitely by appropriate environmental or procedural modifications, or do these cells differ from the heteroploid cells in having an *intrinsically* limited period of reproduction in any environment? Dr. Hayflick (1965) has proposed the latter alternative, with 50 generations as the approximate limit of the number of possible divisions of the diploid cell.

The following questions appear to be critically involved in understanding this situation:

1. What are the biochemical mechanisms responsible for cessation of growth in diploid cells when such arrest occurs after a prolonged period of healthy multiplication under presumably *constant* environmental conditions?

2. What specific genetic determinants present in some or all diploid but not in some heteroploid cells underlie the biochemical action which terminates growth?

3. Can growth cessation be prevented or reversed by appropriate adjustment of the molecular and physical environment?

4. Is this growth cessation related to that which occurs normally in many tissues when multiplying stem cells are transformed to non-multiplying differentiated cells?

5. Is this growth cessation involved in the mammalian aging process?

6. Is some or all malignancy due to production of the heteroploid karyotype like that of the HeLa cell or L cell, which has made possible unlimited reproduction under a large variety of environmental conditions?

Dr. Hayflick has proposed bold and intriguing answers to several of these fundamental questions. However, a clear proof of the answer to any one is not easy to obtain, and the answers to all are vital to many areas of mammalian biology. Among the reasons for the difficulty in securing clear answers to these questions are the following: The cultivation of mammalian cells for a period at least as long as 50 generations is a tedious and costly process. The rich media employed pose the constant threat of contamination. While this threat can be partially controlled with antibiotics, their use throughout so long a period of growth introduces question about their own effect on the process under study. Similarly, the need to use trypsin or other agents to disperse the cell monolayers might introduce cumulative long-term effects. Chromosomal variability in mammalian cells occurs through a variety of processes some of which may be intrinsic and others induced by agents like viruses which are difficult and sometimes impossible to control. The aneuploid forms often outgrow the euploid ones, and constant chromosomal monitoring is necessary. Such monitoring is often difficult to carry out, and small abnormalities may easily escape detection. Finally, the demonstration that growth cessation occurs in one artificial medium or in the body does not furnish proof that different environmental conditions might not be found which would support a significantly larger number of generations of multiplication.

Our studies had impressed upon us the profound influence exercised on the multiplication of mammalian cells by the environmental conditions (Puck et al. 1957, 1958; Tjio & Puck 1958a). The use of single cell plating had demonstrated that in contrast to the apparent uniformity of nutritional requirements which massive cell cultures display, most lines possess unique minimal growth requirements for single cell growth. Small effects often seemed to be very important. For example, the effect of temperature variations attending opening and closing of incubator doors produced a large action on cell growth, as shown in Figure 1, which necessitated designing electronic controls which maintain constancy of temperature, CO_2 pressure, and relative humidity to a much higher degree than that required for the cultivation of bacteria (Ham & Puck 1962a). A relatively small increase in the optimal concentration of several essential nutrients was found to depress severely the growth of particular cells (Ham 1963a, b). Finally, batches of nutrient media were found to change their growth-supporting properties on storage even at $-70°C$.

We do not have definitive experimental data which will unequivocally answer any of the six fundamental questions posed in the earlier paragraphs. However, preliminary data with some bearing

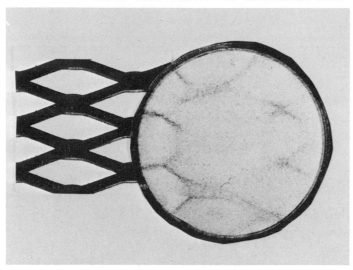

Fig. 1. Demonstration of the sensitivity of mammalian cells to environmental fluctuations in a slowly responding incubator. The metal grid on the left formed the shelf on which a petri dish with a massive cell inoculum rested. The incubator doors were opened and closed during the working day only, in the course of the normal laboratory routine. The pattern on the right shows that the cell density developing in the regions of the glass in contact with the metal, where better temperature control was presumably maintained, greatly exceeds that of the glass over the open spaces.

on question *3* were obtained in the course of an experimental program in which it was required to grow continuously an extremely large number of animal cells. Experiments showed that rabbit cells grew more luxuriously in the media which we had developed than those of any other common laboratory animal, and so this animal was selected for the purpose.

Skin biopsies were taken from 13 different, white, adult rabbits in which both sexes were represented.

Our previous skin biopsy technique was slightly modified as follows: The hair is shaved, the area sterilized with a tincture of 0.02% iodine in 70% ethanol, and a piece of skin of about $1/2$ mm^3 is excised with very sharp, sterile scissors. The fragment is placed in a petri dish, covered with a drop of nutrient medium, and minced with scissors into pieces whose largest dimension is about 0.10 to 0.20 mm. Pieces of the minced tissue are then pipetted on to various points in several 60 mm plastic petri dishes and 1 drop of medium is placed on each piece of tissue and spread over an area of about 1 cm^2. This ensures that the tissue fragment does not float and so fail to become attached to the surface. The petri dish is covered and incubated overnight in an atmosphere containing virtually 100% humidity and 5% CO_2, to prevent drying out. By the next morning, the petri dish is flooded

with 3.0 ml of nutrient medium, care being taken not to dislodge the tissue frag-
ments. This procedure, which omits the use of trypsin makes possible reliable
growth from pinhead sized biopsies, which can be distributed among several petri
dishes.

Each culture initiated rapid growth *in vitro* almost immediately,
producing cells of uniform fibroblast-like morphologies as previously
described for human skin biopsies. In order to insure that the growth
behavior observed was reasonably representative of at least an appreciable portion of the cell population several of the original
biopsies were also trypsinized directly and single cells were plated.
Such biopsies yielded plating efficiencies of approximately 0.10%, in
in contrast to plating efficiencies of 20–30% obtained from the cultures
after they had been grown in the medium employed for some weeks
or months. A typical plating is shown in Figure 2.

Three clones were picked initially and farmed. Their generation
time as determined from cell counts on developing clones was approximately 16.6 hr at the beginning of this experiment. One of these
clones from a female rabbit was selected for long term growth to
supply the large and continuous supply of cells which was required
in other experimental programs.

The farming procedure employed was regulated with great care
and is presented here in detail. Each bottle was inoculated with
3×10^5 cells in 10 ml of F10 medium (Ham 1963a) supplemented
with 5% fetal calf serum and 14% human cord serum. No antibiotics
were employed in the growth medium. Each serum was heated to
60°C for 30 min before use. Only those fetal calf sera were selected
for use which exhibited a single cell plating efficiency of at least 80%
and a normal colony size when used as the serum supplement with our
standard strains of Chinese hamster lung or ovary cells with modal
chromosome numbers of 23 and 21, respectively. The human cord
sera were similarly tested against standard diploid human skin cells,
with a requirement of $\geq 20\%$ in the plating efficiency. The pH of
the medium was adjusted with 5% CO_2 gas in air to 7.3 before addition of the cells. The cells were harvested by trypsinization every
3.5 days without fail, using 2 rinses with 3 ml of 0.05% trypsin
solution (Ham & Puck 1962b) which were discarded, followed by
treatment with 0.6 ml of the same trypsin solution for 5 min at room
temperature. It is important to note that trypsinization was never
carried out at 37°C. New inocula were prepared from such harvested
cells and immediately planted in fresh bottles. The remainder of
the cell harvest was used up in other experiments, although occasional
samples were frozen. All incubations were carried out in our elec-

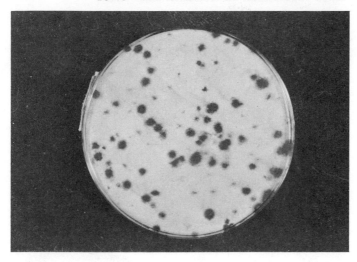

Fig. 2. Typical colonies resulting from plating of single rabbit cells from the culture described. The rough edges of the colonies are typical of the fibroblast-like cells, which result from skin biopsies under the conditions here described.

tronically regulated incubators. Where not otherwise specified the procedures were those described earlier (Ham & Puck 1962b).

Under these carefully controlled farming conditions 2.7 ($\pm$ 0.5) $\times$ 10^6 cells were harvested from each bottle every 3.5 days, a recovery of 9 times the initial inoculum. This cell recovery is equivalent to a generation time of 26.5 hr which represents a considerably smaller growth rate than the generation time of 16.6 hr obtained from such cultures in the same medium when studied in plates. In all probability an appreciable fraction of the cells was lost in harvest by the trypsinization procedure, either through lysis or failure of the harvesting procedure to be complete under the mild conditions employed. However, we shall use the conservative calculations of considering each 3.5-day incubation period to have resulted in a ninefold increase in cell number. This clone of rabbit cells was continuously farmed with rigid control of conditions as described for a total of 616 days representing 554 generations. During this period no incident of growth failure or change in morphology was noted. Towards the end of this period measurement of the generation time was carried out by counting cells in colonies and by life cycle analysis (Puck & Steffen 1963; Puck 1964). These measurements revealed the culture to possess a generation time of 15.8 hr which is indistinguishable from that obtained at the beginning of this period of cultivation.

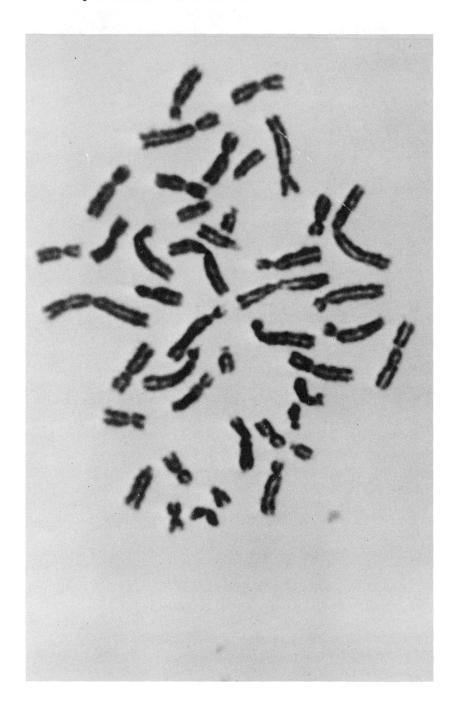

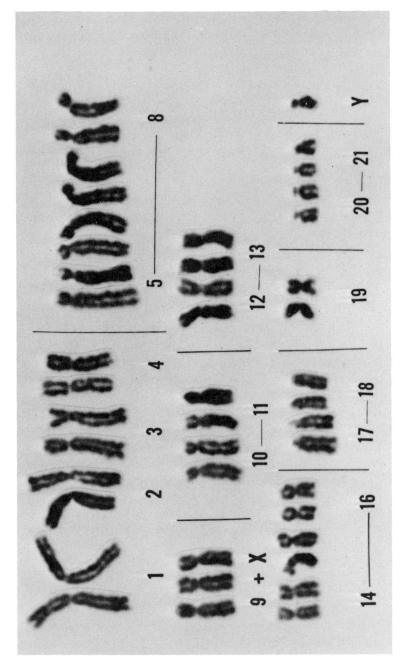

Fig. 3A. Typical metaphase and karyotypic analysis of short term blood cultures from a male rabbit.

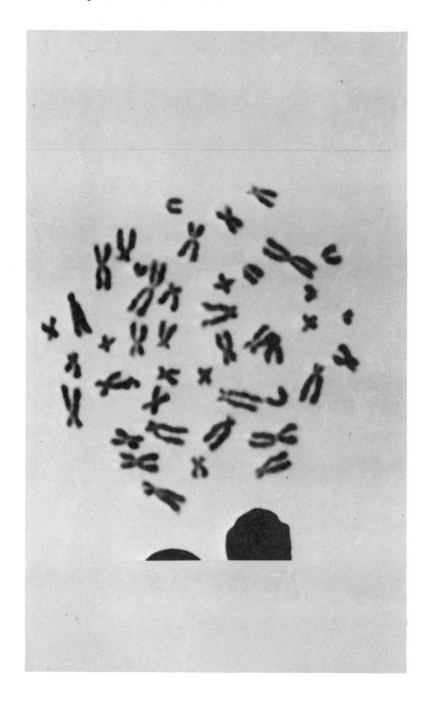

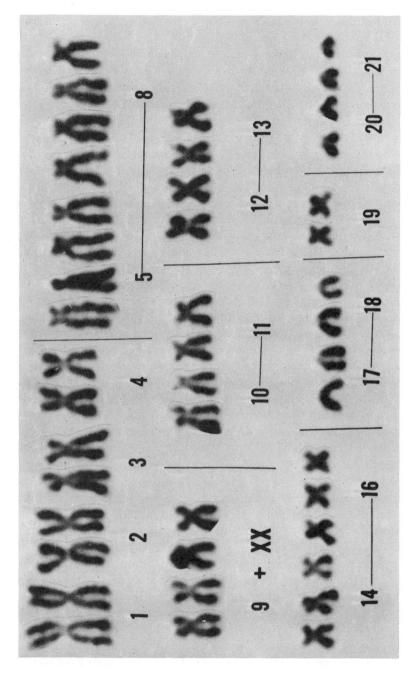

Fig 3B. Typical metaphase and karyotypic analysis of short term blood cultures from a female rabbit.

Unfortunately, since this experiment was carried out for a different purpose, routine chromosomal analyses were not available. However, after this prolonged period of cultivation, the karyotype of these cells was examined. The karyotype of the rabbit has been previously defined as consisting of $2N = 44$ chromosomes (Melander 1956; Clausen & Syverton 1962; Prunierias, Jacquemont & Mathivon 1966).

Chromosome counts were made on 155 well-spread metaphases, of which 154 had 44 and one had 43 chromosomes. (Two other cells with 43 chromosomes were observed but these had broken cell boundaries which could have caused chromosomal loss, and so these were not scored, as discussed elsewhere (Puck 1962)). The incidence of polyploidy was in the neighborhood of 1% or less. This constancy of chromosome number is as good as that obtained from short term diploid cultures or from direct animal biopsy without culture. It is distinctly different from the condition of variability in chromosome number found in heteroploid cells like the HeLa, or in near-diploid cells like the Chinese hamster.

Detailed analysis of the chromosome constitution of the rabbit cells was carried out after their sojourn in culture for more than 500 generations. Short-term blood cultures from a male and female rabbit were also prepared and selected metaphases were analyzed for comparison with the long-term tissue culture cells. Typical blood culture chromosome sets from a male and female rabbit, respectively, and their corresponding karyotypes are shown in Figures 3A and 3B. These karyotypes are in general agreement with those described by Prunieras et al. (1966) and are described in Table 1. Because of the recurrence of similarities in chromosomal shapes, the analysis presents some difficulty.

Twenty metaphases of cells from the long term tissue culture were analyzed, of which a typical example is shown in Figure 4. The karyotype obtained was constant, and while on preliminary analysis it appeared to resemble that of the normal rabbit, more searching examination revealed a distinct difference from the blood culture cells. The tissue culture cells possess an extra metacentric chromosome of a size between that of pairs No. 2 and No. 3; and are lacking one chromosome in the group 17–18, probably from pair No. 17 which is the larger of the two pairs. (See the two positions with question marks in Figure 4.) The other chromosomes resemble those of the normal karyotype.

It is possible that the extra metacentric chromosome is an isochromosome of the almost telocentric No. 17, or it could have arisen

Table 1. The karyotype of the rabbit as found from the analysis of short term blood culture (see Figure 4)

Pairs 1–4	Large, submedian to almost median chromosomes. All 4 pairs are identifiable.
Pairs 5–8	Large, subterminal chromosomes. Pair No. 6 or 7 has satellites on the short arm.
Pairs 9 + X	Medium sized, submedian chromosomes. One of these is the X chromosome, presumably the one with a larger short/long arm ratio.
Pairs 10–11	Medium sized, subterminal chromosomes.
Pairs 12–13	Medium sized, submedian to almost median chromosomes.
Pairs 14–16	Small size, submedian to median chromosomes. Pair No. 15 has rather large satellites on the short arm. Pair No. 16 is median.
Pairs 17–18	Small size, subterminal chromosomes. The short arms are very small.
Pair 19	Smallest median chromosome.
Pairs 20–21	Smallest subterminal chromosomes. One of these pairs is satellited.
Y	Submedian of the size of 20–21.

through nondisjunction and subsequent fusion at the centromeric region of No. 17.

The mechanism and time of origin of these two karyotypic abnormalities is unfortunately unknown. Nor does this experience prove any necessary relationship between the abnormal karyotype and cell longevity. Two alternative possibilities appear to be furnished by these data: (*1*) The chromosomal abnormality may be a coincidence. This possibility should be clarifiable by repetition of this experiment, checking the chromosomes at frequent and regular intervals. (*2*) Alternatively, the longevity may be due to the specific chromosomal abnormality here described, as demanded by the Hayflick hypothesis. In that case, this experiment tentatively defines a specific chromosomal alteration which is responsible for the cell's prolonged reproductive life.

These experiments are continuing. It should be pointed out that a clonal strain of this kind, with its small deviation from true diploidy, highly uniform karyotype, and rapid growth rate, furnishes an excellent system for many kinds of genetic or biochemical analysis.

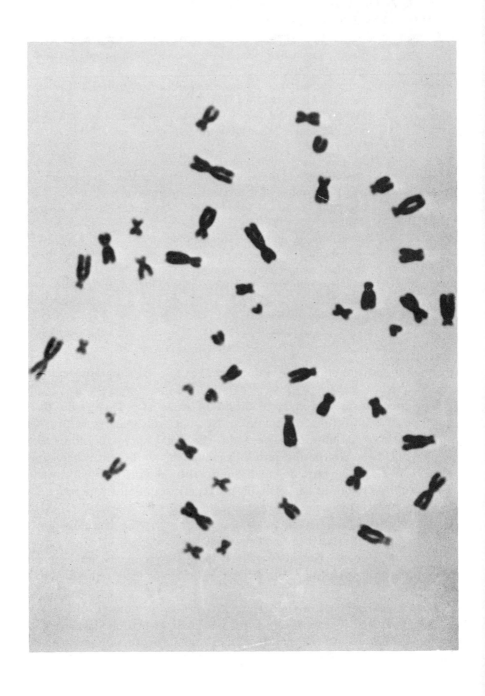

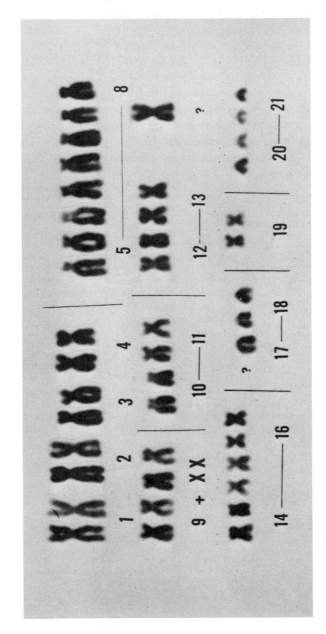

Fig. 4. Typical metaphase and karyotypic analysis of the cloned rabbit cell culture after more than 500 generations of growth *in vitro*. While the similarities in structure of many of these chromosomes make possible an apparently normal pairing of all the members of this karyotype, a highly searching analysis indicates that in all probability a discrepancy exists as shown by the two question marks and discussed in the text.

SUMMARY

In a single test episode, cloned rabbit cells were grown for more than 500 generations in tissue culture without apparent change in growth rate or morphology. Analysis of the karyotype at the end of this growth period revealed a highly constant chromosomal constitution with a chromosome number of 44, but with one extra and one missing chromosome. The abnormal chromosomes have been tentatively identified. This chromosomal abnormality is either a pure coincidence or it is responsible for the reproductive longevity. In the latter case, a specific chromosomal change has been linked to the property of prolonged growth of an *in vitro* culture.

References

Clausen, J. J. and Syverton, J. T. (1962). *J. Nat. Cancer Inst., 28,* 117–145.

Earle, W. R., Bryant, J. C. and Schilling, E. L. (1954). *Ann. N.Y. Acad. Sci., 58,* 1000–10111.

Fischer, A. (1946). In *Biology of Tissue Cells,* Gydenalske Boghandel Nordisk Forlag, Copenhagen, Chapter 1, p. 16–17.

Fisher, H. W., Puck, T. T. and Sato, G. (1959). *J. Exp. Med., 109,* 649–660.

Ford, C. E. (1962). *Nat. Cancer Inst. Monogr., No. 7,* 105–118.

Ham, R. G. (1963a). *Exp. Cell Res., 29,* 515–526.

Ham, R. G. (1963b). *Science, 140,* 802–803.

Ham, R. G. (1965). *Proc. Nat. Acad. Sci. U.S.A., 53,* 288–293.

Ham, R. G. and Puck, T. T. (1962a). *Proc. Soc. Exp. Biol. Med., 111,* 67–71.

Ham, R. G. and Puck, T. T. (1962b). In *Methods in Enzymology,* Vol. 5, Colowick, S. P. and Kaplan, N. D., Eds., Academic Press, New York, p. 90–119.

Hayflick, L. (1965). *Exp. Cell Res., 37,* 614–636. See also This Symposium, p. 83.

Hsu, T. C. and Moorhead, P. S. (1957). *J. Nat. Cancer Inst., 18,* 463–470.

Melander, Y. (1956). *Hereditas, 42,* 432–435.

Moore, A. E., Southam, C. M. and Sternberg, S. (1956). *Science, 124,* 127–129.

Moorhead, P. S., Nowell, P. C., Mellman, W. J., Battips, D. M. and Hungerford, D. A. (1960). *Exp. Cell Res., 20,* 613–616.

Parker, F. C., Castor, L. N. and McCulloch, E. A. (1957). *Spec. Publs. N.Y. Acad. Sci., 5,* 379–397.

Prunierias, M., Jacquemont, C. and Mathivon, M. F. (1965). *Ann. Inst. Pasteur, Paris, 109,* 465–471.

Puck, T. T. (1962). In *Methodology in Human Genetics,* Burdette, W. J., Ed., Holden-Day, San Francisco, California, p. 260–271.

Puck, T. T. (1964). *Cold Spring Harb. Sympt. Quant. Biol., 29,* 167–176.

Puck, T. T., Cieciura, S. J. and Fisher, H. W. (1957). *J. Exp. Med., 106,* 145–158.

Puck, T. T., Cieciura, S. J. and Robinson, A. (1958). *J. Exp. Med., 108,* 945–956.

Puck, T. T. and Marcus, P. I. (1955). *Proc. Nat. Acad. Sci. U.S.A., 41,* 432–437.

Puck, T. T., Marcus, P. I. and Cieciura, S. J. (1956). *J. Exp. Med., 103,* 273–284.

Puck, T. T. and Robinson, A. (1966). In *Biologic Basis of Pediatric Practice—*

Infancy, Childhood, and Adolescence, Cooke, R. E., Ed., McGraw-Hill, New York, in press.

Puck, T. T. and Steffen, J. (1963). *Biophys. J., 3*, 379–397.

Sanford, K. K., Earle, W. R. and Likely, G. D. (1948). *J. Nat. Cancer Inst., 9*, 229–246.

Swim, H. E. and Parker, R. F. (1957). *Spec., Publs. N.Y. Acad. Sci., 5*, 351–355.

Tjio, J. H. and Puck, T. T. (1958a). *J. Exp. Med., 108*, 259–268.

Tjio, J. H. and Puck, T. T. (1958b). *Proc. Nat. Acad. Sci. U.S.A., 44*, 1229–1237.

DISCUSSION

DR. GLASER: Do you mean to imply that, if you take out a frozen aliquot, it will go exactly to the 50 doublings characteristic of the uninterrupted cultures?

DR. HAYFLICK: Not necessarily exactly, because the method of precisely determining these doublings is very imperfect. I would not take differences less than ± 5 or 8 doublings to be significant. Human fetal fibroblasts reconstituted from liquid nitrogen undergo a cumulative total of about 50 doublings including those undergone prior to preservation.

DR. STREHLER: How many doublings are there between a fetal lung and an adult lung in normal development? Has some of the doubling capacity been used up?

DR. HAYFLICK: It depends on where you are beginning with fetal lung, what the size or weight of the starting population is. Beginning from a single cell it is easy to do the calculations to give the number of doublings necessary to equal the weight of adult lung. However, the embryonic lungs that were used in our studies came from 3 month old embryos, and I doubt if the number of cell doublings between a 3 month embryonic lung and an adult lungs exceeds six or eight.

DR. GROBSTEIN: What is your experience with human embryonic kidneys?

DR. HAYFLICK: The kidney usually ends up as a culture of epithelial cells whose proliferative capacity is generally very much more limited. Usually there are only three or four doublings obtainable with kidney cells cultivated *in vitro*. We have been talking only about those cells that have a definite capacity for proliferation in tissue culture. Some human kidney cultures are composed predominantly of fibroblasts which undergo the usual 50 divisions.

DR. WULFF: You are placing a great deal of emphasis on morphology of the culture.

DR. HAYFLICK: Yes, but not entirely, because the cultured fibroblasts lay down collagen and an intercellular matrix and that is probably what one thinks fibroblasts do *in vivo*.

DR. PUCK: Do you have any idea how homogeneous the population is?

DR. HAYFLICK: No. Subjective impressions are that the inhomogeneity is like that of the bacterial cultures we have already discussed. This problem can be tackled only by time-lapse cinemicrophotography in which individual cells are followed and the lineage of the resulting progeny determined. I would expect that one would find the same kinds of patterns of death in tissue culture cells as one finds in bacteria; that not all the progeny are viable nor do they all give rise to further progeny.

We have also done cloning experiments, allowing isolated, single cells to proliferate. Their doubling potential is the same as that of the wild population.

DR. TILL: I would like to describe our system and very briefly summarize the results of one particular use McCulloch, Siminovitch, and I have made of it. The system is as follows (Till & McCulloch 1961. *Radiat. Res., 14*, 213–222): We take cells from the blood-forming tissue (marrow, spleen, or fetal liver) of a normal mouse of an inbred strain, disperse the cells, count them, and then inject a known number of cells intravenously into another mouse of the same inbred strain. Prior to injection of cells, the recipient mouse is given a large dose (900–1000 rads) of total-body radiation. The function of the irradiation is to inhibit the proliferative capacity of the animal's own blood-forming tissues and so to convert the animal into a culture vessel for the transplanted cells. If one has injected the proper number of cells, then after about 10 days the spleens of the recipient animals contain macroscopically visible colonies of cells. We have a good deal of evidence to show that these colonies arise from individual injected cells, which lodge in the spleen, proliferate, and give rise to colonies of descendants. I will discuss some of this evidence in a moment. First, however, I would like to make the point that the cells in these colonies differ in a very important way from the cells in the colonies described by Dr. Puck; in the latter type of colonies, all the cells in each colony can be considered to be identical or nearly identical to the cells of origin. In contrast, each spleen colony is quite heterogeneous, consisting of a large number of differentiating cells of different kinds. The differentiating cells are mainly erythroblasts, but also present in varying proportions in different colonies are granulocytes, megakaryocytes, and relatively undifferentiated cells that are difficult to identify (Till & McCulloch 1961). The finding that spleen colonies contain differentiating cells immediately poses a very intriguing problem. If the colonies do in fact result from the proliferation and differentiation of the descendants of a single cell, then the system provides a means of answering a long-standing question in hematology, that is: Does the blood-forming system of an adult mammal contain stem cells that are multipotent, in that they can differentiate in more than one direction? Evidence for this view was obtained by forming colonies from stem cells in which chromosomal markers were induced by prior irradiation with gamma-rays. In colonies which contained markers, more than 95% of the dividing cells in a given colony exhibited the same markers (Becker, McCulloch & Till 1963. *Nature, 197*, 452–454). This finding implies that 95% or more of the dividing cells in such a marked colony were members of a clone of cells resulting from the proliferation of a single cell, derived from the irradiated marrow, in which the marker had been generated.

This result provides support for the view that adult marrow does contain multipotent stem cells. It does not, however, provide conclusive proof for this view, since many of the differentiated cells in the colony are non-dividing cells, and of course one cannot use the chromosome-marker technique to determine whether or not these nondividing cells also belong to the clone. Some other approach must be used to test for the origin of the nondividing cells. For this reason we tried to do with spleen colonies what any microbiologist might do if he were faced with the problem of isolating a clone. We dissected our individual colonies, derived originally from marrow, dispersed them, and injected them back into heavily irradiated recipients, one colony per recipient. As might be expected, we got more colonies, so that the "first-generation" colonies gave rise quite successfully to "second-generation" colonies. On histological examination, these again appeared to be composed of erythroblasts, granulocytes, megakaryocytes, and undifferentiated cells, and seemed to be very similar to the first-generation colonies. Though the efficiency of formation of second-generation colonies from the cells of first-generation colonies was quite low, something of the order of 30 spleen colonies formed per 10^7 cells injected, it was easily detectable. We then picked out second-generation colonies and again transplanted the cells from individual colonies into heavily irradiated animals. Very few third-generation colonies were found (Siminovitch, Till & McCulloch, 1964. *J. Cell. Comp. Physiol., 64*, 23–32). This means that the frequency of colony formation had dropped from about 30 colonies per 10^7 cells to less than one colony per 10^7 cells in going from the second to the third generation. It is possible that the same number of colony-forming cells were present at the third transfer as at the second transfer, but that a greater proportion of the cells were damaged in preparing the cell suspensions, or that a smaller proportion of the injected cells reached the spleen after the third transfer than the second. Both these possibilities seem unlikely, since the first- and second-generation colonies were dissected and suspended using the same procedure, and the cell suspensions were assayed for colony-forming ability in exactly the same way, by injection of similar numbers of cells into irradiated mice of the same inbred strain. It seems clear that the second-generation colonies differ some way from the first-generation colonies. Indeed, it seems quite likely that the way in which they differ is in respect to the extent, or rate, of proliferation of the colony-forming stem cells which they contain, and that this capacity for proliferation decreases with time as the cells are repeatedly stimulated to grow by transplantation into heavily irradiated hosts. Whether or not this observation has any relationship to the findings that Dr. Hayflick described for cells in culture remains to be determined. For example, one very important question has not yet been answered: Is this change a reversible one?

DR. KOHN: There may be two situations *in vivo* which differ a good deal from Dr. Hayflick's *in vitro* experiment. One may be in the gut wherein the epithelial cells are turning over rapidly. The turnover time may be something from 3 to 6 days so in the course of 10 years the basal cells might divide more than a thousand times. In the case of hydra, too, there is good evidence that the organisms are essentially immortal. Cells travel down the body stem and are discarded. Multiplication goes on indefinitely. The consequent many hundreds of divisions possibly indicate that *in vivo* situations, where cell to cell interactions that cannot be duplicated in cultures exist, are so radically different that the two situations cannot be compared.

DR. WILLIAMS: The stem cell concept provides a rather different situation in which, for example, a stratum Malpighii cell could be quite different from a cell that goes on to be cornified.

DR. HAYFLICK: That question has been raised before not only with gut cells, but also with blood forming and skin cells. It is probably a fallacious argument because of the assumption that all the cells are dividing or are dividing synchronously. One clone of the total population could contribute to the casting off of border cells into the gut; the others lie at rest until the first has gone through an arbitrary number of doublings. Another one will then take over. This process has been considered in some detail by H. E. M. Kay (1965. *The Lancet, ii*, 418–419).

DR. STREHLER: In the basal layer of the skin it is not possible, on the basis of morphological examination, to determine which cells are going to divide. It looks fairly random, one basal cell or another can divide. It does not appear to be the case that a very small population is dividing at any particular time. It does not matter whether the 50 generations is produced by allowing all the cells to divide simultaneously or by taking a small fraction of the cells and making them go through a larger number of divisions.

DR. HAYFLICK: I was careful to use the term doublings and not generations; an important distinction. I agree entirely that it is very possible that, to take an extreme view, when these cultures were subcultivated only one cell was doubling every 30 min. while the others just vegetated. That would ultimately double the population. The other extreme position is that all the cells divided only once. I am sure that the answer lies somewhere between the two extremes.

DR. DULBECCO: Are there stem cells which do not divide?

DR. MAYNARD SMITH: There could be, but is there any evidence that this is so?

DR. GALLOP: Are there any other criteria, perhaps, biochemical, that could be set up in these repeated cultures, particularly in the ones that Dr. Puck spoke of, that are so carefully controlled? Perhaps one could compare the pattern of amino acids in fifth and tenth cultures, looking, that is, at what was left in the media rather than at the chromosomes.

DR. PUCK: This would be extremely difficult. We take tremendous precautions not to let the concentration of the medium components change and we feel that only when we do this do we get such long-term growth. However, while we feel that a properly balanced medium will sustain growth for a longer period than a poorly balanced one, we do not know whether an upper limit exists of necessity regardless of the medium.

Our data demonstrate that neither the instability in chromosome number nor the large degree of aneuploidy and polyploidy which characterize most stable heteroploid cultures is necessary for long-term growth *in vitro*. They neither prove nor disprove that a cell which is strictly euploid and possesses normal chromosomal structure within the limits of present day analysis, can grow for more than 50 generations. It would be extremely difficult, if not impossible, to prove that no conditions will ever be found so that such cells can grow for longer periods *in vitro*. However, it would appear essential to define the genetic loci and the biochemical effects, thereof, which limit the growth of euploid cells under conditions where the growth of heteroploid cells is unaffected.

DR. MEDAWAR: What reasonable hypothesis about the nature of determinate growth in tissue culture would be eliminated by the freezing experiment? It seems to me that the results would fit many hypotheses. Second, what kind of picture of decay is there in tissue culture of normal cells in media *known* to be inadequate? The presumption underlying Dr. Hayflick's experiment is that the media used in which growth was determinate were either adequate or as adequate as human ingenuity can make them. If one got the same kind of picture of decay, though on a smaller scale, with a medium known to be inadequate, this would rather tell in favor of Dr. Puck's conception of the process. I recollect that most people who begin to do tissue culture use inadequate media or do not carry out procedures properly. The cultures last a few weeks or, if they are lucky, a month or so and then to their dismay and without any very obvious premonition, the cultures start going downhill in a way which resembles the phenomenon Dr. Hayflick has been describing.

DR. HAYFLICK: The original work (Hayflick, L. & Moorhead, P. S., 1961. *Exp. Cell Res., 25,* 585–621) that led to the suggestion that media did not play a role employed the following logic. First, in this same medium one can grow heteroploid populations indefinitely. This is not a very telling argument that the medium used is adequate, because it is generally agreed that the heteroploid populations are less temperamental and less sophisticated in their nutritional requirements. But anyway, it is clear that diploid populations decline in the same medium which sustains heteroploid populations so well. The next observation was that at any given moment in time there were approximately 25, or 30, or 40 of these diploid cell strains derived from 5, 10, or 15 different embryos. Only those at the 40th, 50th, or let us say 60th subcultivation or doubling were, in fact, reaching Phase III and dying. Finally, the medium that has been used for the last 2 years comes from a single pool of powdered medium which is reconstituted when required. So any factor in the medium that would conceivably be at fault is constant throughout the entire experiment.

Three other types of experiments, using mixed cultures, have been done and bear heavily on this question (Hayflick, L., 1965. *Exp. Cell Res., 37,*

614–636). The first has been to mix male and female cell populations which are distinguishable only by chromosome analysis. For example, male cells at the 40th passage were mixed with equal numbers of female cells at the 15th passage; unmixed cultures being kept as controls. After 25 more sub-cultivations (each subcultivation yielding one doubling) all of the cells in the mixed population were found to be female. The same medium was used throughout but the male cells had reached Phase III and were lost. It would be difficult to explain a preferential effect of media based on the sex of the cell. The experiment also implies that, if the degeneration of these cultures is due to a microorganism or a virus (which is an obvious possibility), it must be an extraordinary virus which can discriminate between the sexes.

In the second experiment three clones, that is, three individual cells, were selected arbitrarily from a population of human diploid cells that had undergone only two doublings from the starting embryonic tissue in tissue culture. The individual cells were allowed to grow to a population density (approximately 4×10^6 cells) that we ordinarily use in the laboratory when subcultivating cells at a one to two split ratio. From that population one to two subcultivations were made with equal densities inoculated into the daughter bottles. The three clones, after having reached four million cells, then were found to undergo, respectively, 30, 27, and 26 doublings before reaching Phase III. Taking into consideration the total number of doublings (22) necessary to raise a single cell to four million, the total number of doublings comes to the sort of figure (52, 49, 48) that is expected even when these cloned populations are exposed to 22 fewer experiences with trypsin and 22 fewer experiences with fresh media.

The third experiment involved withdrawing from the liquid nitrogen container three ampules representing three widely separated passage levels, the 11th, 21st, and 45th. These populations were then mixed in the three possible combinations, and both mixtures and unmixed control cultures were subcultivated as usual. The numbers of doublings occurring in these mixtures before the entire culture had vanished are only compatible with the view that one is measuring the survival of the younger component of the mixture and that the outcome of the growth of the cells is not influenced by the presence of old cells or of the nature of the medium.

DR. ORGEL: In following this fascinating discussion as to whether lung cells are eternal or not, we have strayed from the important point that, in studies of aging, there is one culture medium which is particularly relevant to human lung cultures and that is human lung. Hayflick has produced evidence that we can get an aging effect in intact lung. Are there any criticisms of the experiment which showed that the numbers of generations which cells survived after removal from embryonic or from adult lung are different? If these experiments are accepted, then the argument as to whether cells may be eternal in one medium but not in another is irrelevant to the problem of human aging.

DR. KOHN: In terms of the number of doublings obtained in culture, Dr. Hayflick can distinguish an embryonic lung from an adult lung but not between mature and old lungs. So his system may tell us more about growth and growth cessation than it will about aging.

I would also like to point out that the viability of his system is very much dependent on the ability of the cells to divide; apparently if they cannot divide, they die. In a higher animal, however, a neuron or a muscle cell has its last division at about the time of birth and then exists as long as the life-span of the individual which may be about 80 or 90 years.

DR. PUCK: I want to come to Dr. Hayflick's support. In a very real sense I do not think there is necessarily any controversy here, but there does remain an area that requires intensive exploration. It becomes necessary to define precisely the number of replications possible for different cells in media of various composition and to document whether systematic changes in cell composition occur at the end of any particular number of generations.

DR. CURTIS: Taking Dr. Hayflick's arguments at their face value, the reason perhaps why these cells finally go downhill and expire could be simply that they gradually build up a certain number of mutations. What would be the reason for this chromosomal instability? Perhaps an error of replication? The more the replications the greater the possibility of making an error, and an error once made would go on indefinitely. However, in the system I described this morning, this cannot be true because we are dealing there with cells which do not replicate and yet they are building up mutations from aberrations within the cell all the time.

DR. ATWOOD: I want to suggest a different way of thinking about this which, I think, supports Dr. Hayflick; that is to consider whether a feasible model can be constructed based on the assumption that the clone terminates because the medium is wrong. First, start with cells that are known to grow indefinitely (e.g., *E. coli*) and then try to devise a medium that would, under continuous replacement, let the bacteria go for about 50 doublings and no more. I find that an extremely difficult, if not impossible, model to build. Alternatively, let us simply admit the obvious, and say that when these cells divide, they do not accurately copy themselves at some point or points in the process. If they did so, the clone would be immortal.

DR. GLASER: It is a bit of comic relief to say that bacteria do not live indefinitely either. In attempts to do a long term experiment in a chemostat, types are constantly dying out and being replaced by so-called fitter types characterized by either a different growth rate or different biochemical abilities. Whether one is likely to get a dying out of a type or evolution to a fitter form depends upon knowing the generation time in comparison with mutations or whatever effects may change the physiology. If only three cell lines at one laboratory and one at another have been looked at there is a chance that there was a mutation in one laboratory only that need not have changed the karyotype but was subtler and changed its biochemical abilities.

TRANSPLANTATION AND AGING

P. L. Krohn

Department of Anatomy,
The Medical School,
The University of Birmingham,
Birmingham, England

It is only relatively recently that the study of aging has lost its association with quackery and rejuvenation cure-alls and has become accepted as a reputable subject which, in some parts of the world at least, now receives the support, in terms of scientists and resources, which it deserves. The study of transplantation had equally to pass through a period when wild men made unsupportable claims before it became established some way ahead of aging as an area in which new and exciting achievements are only just around the corner.

Unlike gerontologists, who seem to hold out little hope of immediate or sensational success, those who are attacking problems in transplantation immunology seem to be confident that they will soon have mastered the main obstacles which prevent the transfer of tissue from one person to another. When they succeed, students of transplantation will have enormously benefited geriatrics, or the treatment of the aged, in an intensely practical fashion by making possible the replacement of prematurely defective organs by prostheses of one or another sort.

But, besides its practical and therapeutic possibilities, transplantation also contributes a technical way of getting to grips with a wide variety of problems in gerontology just as it has, in the past, served to analyze the problems of embryology or endocrinology. The special value of the technique lies in the opportunities that it provides for experimentally dissociating a tissue from its normal coeval environment. Such transplants to either a younger or older host have been termed heterochronic transplants and the hosts called age chimaeras.

My purpose is to show how the technique can usefully be applied to the study of some selected gerontological problems; but first, an important limitation must be appreciated and accepted. It is essential to restrict oneself to those situations which are not complicated by interference from the homograft reaction. This means effectively that experiments must be done on inbred strains of small rodents— rats, guinea pigs, and especially mice. Fortunately, there are sufficient genetically different strains with differing aging properties to provide material for a great range of studies.

Early endocrinologists who used transplantation methods were un-aware of these limitations and seem to have transferred their own ignorance to the animals used in their experiments and somehow enabled them to behave in ways we would think unlikely today. Nowadays, however, there is no excuse for making the interpretation of one's experiments more difficult than it already is by introducing unnecessary uncertainties of this sort, and the importance of fully controlling the genetic homogeneity of one's experimental animals cannot be overemphasized.

It need hardly be added that the general idea of using the technique of transplantation in this way is not new. Perhaps the first effective experiments were done by Foà (1900, 1901) but since then it has been applied with success, and with more attention to problems of histo-compatibility, by Geiringer (1956) to the adrenal cortex, Pepper (1961a,b) to the thymus, Mawdsley & Harrison (1963) to the bone, Franks & Chesterman (1964) to the prostate, and DeOme (1965) to the mammary gland.

I shall deal with three separate situations. In the first, the technique has been applied to problems of the aging of female reproductive function—by transplantation of a whole organ (the ovary) or of its product, the ovulated and fertilized egg. Then I shall go on to describe how heterochronic transplants of skin can be used to analyze the changes in respiratory activity of aging skin and finally to con-sider what can be achieved by the use of serial transplantation of the skin, as a representative organized tissue, from one host to another. Such experiments should show whether or not its life-span is limited.

TRANSPLANTATION AND AGING OF
FEMALE REPRODUCTIVE FUNCTION

The details of changes in female reproductive function with age have been set out elsewhere (Krohn 1964) and the general pattern for mice, in particular, has often been described. At puberty, fertility is low but very soon litter size builds up to a plateau and remains at a high level for some varying period of time until a gradual decline ushers in final failure. In polytocous rodents the decline in overall fertility is seen not only as a decline in litter size but also in failure to conceive again immediately after parturition and in a failure of maternal behavior and lactation. A special feature in women, to which we shall return later, is the increasing probability that a foetus will be abnormal, and particularly that it will be a mongol, as the mother's age exceeds 40.

The first obvious point for analytical attack on the factors underlying this decline in function is the ovary and its complement of germ cells. There is now no doubt that the total number of oocytes which will be available during the reproductive life-span has been fixed at or around the time of birth. In round figures, for women about a million oocytes are available and for mice about ten thousand. Even in the course of the most fertile reproductive life-span only a small proportion will be utilized. The rest are destroyed by a process of atresia which has presented so untractable a problem that we still know very little about it. I emphasize our ignorance here because an understanding of factors controlling the rate of this process would obviously create large opportunities for both extending and for contracting the reproductive life-span.

It is self-evident that reproduction must come to an end when the ovaries no longer contain any oocytes, but animals stop producing litters a considerable time before this final phase has been approached. Detailed study of the cycles in mice shows that the period immediately succeeding the overtly fertile period is characterized by seemingly normal ovulations and conceptions. However, the embryos fail to develop normally and are usually aborted in the middle of the pregnancy.

The obvious approach, which is suggested by transplantation methodology, is to test the adequacy of the aging gonads by removing them and replacing them with new young ones. Another equally obvious experiment is to transfer the old ovaries which have been removed into a young environment and see whether they can be rejuvenated in any way.

The technical problems which face anyone wishing to transplant ovaries orthotopically (i.e., precisely to replace the original ovary so that full reproductive function is possible) have been discussed elsewhere (Krohn 1962, 1965) and have been sufficiently overcome for the method to be considered a practical one. More than three-quarters of the operations should be successful and up to 17 litters with 89 offspring have been obtained in Young-Young control transplants in mice of fertile strains. These are figures which compare favorably with the full lifetime's breeding performance of normal mice.

THE ORTHOTOPIC TRANSFER OF YOUNG OVARIES TO OLD HOSTS

The result of a first series of experiments of this sort have been described already (Krohn 1962) and the results are now given of a new series, under more carefully controlled conditions, using as hosts only old breeders whose reproductive history was completely known and who had entered the period of their life when conceptions repeatedly end in abortions and not in normal deliveries.

Of 24 such exchanges, three were complete surgical failures, i.e., the graft did not become revascularized. Eight recipients which mated but did not conceive were found to have capsular adhesions. Sections of the grafts showed recently ruptured follicles and normal numbers of ovulations, which were trapped in cystic dilatations of the ovarian bursa caused by adhesions.

Vaginal bleeding in the remaining 13 showed that they had conceived and had implanted blastocysts in the uterus on one or more occasions, but only two mice in the group produced any litters. One mouse produced three and the other one litter. The largest litter contained only three offspring. The 13 mice making up this group of successful transplants were all killed during subsequent periods of vaginal bleeding at around the 12th–15th day of pregnancy. The numbers of normal and degenerating embryos in the uterine horns were counted and compared with the number of corpora lutea of pregnancy found in the ovaries. The totals for the group are three normal embryos, two doubtfully normal embryos, 43 placental moles or degenerating embryos, and 104 corpora lutea of pregnancy. The discrepancy between the numbers of corpora lutea and the numbers of embryos plus placental moles presumably is a measure of the number of conceptuses which are lost early in pregnancy without leaving visible evidence in the uterus. The histological appearance of the ovaries, indicating that the numbers of ovulations and corpora lutea were normal, clearly implies that not much is wrong with the pituitary control of the grafted ovary. Nevertheless, many blastocysts disappear completely early in the course of pregnancy and most of the remainder that succeed in implanting fail to develop to term in the uterus.

On the other hand, it should be noted that Ascheim's (1964) work on heterotopic ovarian transplants in rats suggests that dysfunction of the hypothalamic control of the anterior pituitary may be involved in the decline of reproductive function. However, the work with mice provides no evidence of inadequate or inappropriate pituitary secretions.

The results can most simply be interpreted as indicating that deterioration of the uterine environment plays an important part in determining the final outcome of the pregnancy. The total disappearance of many of the blastocysts, however, might still indicate that, as the animal gets older, an increasing proportion of the ovulated eggs become inadequate. The presence of almost normal numbers of healthy looking zygotes in the tubes (Talbert & Krohn 1966) does not lend support to this view, but the evident inadequacy of the blastocyst which finally develops into a human mongol requires one to take the possibility seriously.

Two alternative experimental approaches are possible. First, one can remove the ovaries from old mice which are still in the phase when conception is possible but the pregnancy does not come to term, and use them for transplantation to young hosts. Such ovaries are large—made up mainly of nongerminal material—and difficult to transplant to the smaller ovarian capsules of the young hosts. They inevitably contain relatively few oocytes and a considerable proportion of this residue will be destroyed by ischaemic necrosis before the circulation through the graft is restored.

So the failure rate is bound to be high and the experiment therefore an extravagant one. Nevertheless, it will be a rewarding one even if only a few grafts succeed. For it should show that eggs from an ovary which could not develop successfully in the original environment behave satisfactorily in a more favorable milieu elsewhere.

In an attempt to get an adequate experimental answer, 83 ovaries from old mice, whose reproductive phase was coming to an end in a series of abortions, were transplanted to young hosts. Of these transfers, eight were total technical failures. Ten hosts showed only oestrous vaginal cycles and did not mate. Forty-three showed vaginal plugs as well, indicating successful mating, but there were no pregnancies. The ovarian capsular membrane of many of these mice had been inadequately restored but the presence of eggs in the tubes of some of them when they were killed at the time of mating, indicated that they were responding normally to gonadotrophins.

A further eight mice had one vaginal bleeding after mating but brought no litters to term, and seven mice had one pregnancy each with litters of only one.

None of these foregoing results really contributes to the solution of the problem, since there is no way of knowing how many ovulations there were in that particular pregnancy. The remaining mice do, however, provide positive information about the capacity of eggs from old donors to survive and to develop.

One young host mouse which had received a unilateral graft, like all the other mice in this series, was killed during its first pregnancy. The single pregnant uterine horn contained five healthy foetuses compared with two, three, and one foetuses born to the donor from both horns in the last three completed pregnancies before it was killed. The five foetuses should also be contrasted with the seven decaying placental moles out of a total eight implants found in the uterus of the donor when it was killed.

The last six successful experimental mice had two, two, three, four, five, and seven pregnancies, most of the litters containing four or more foetuses and up to nine. Such numbers are considerably larger than any that could be expected normally to occur, and they provide further strong evidence in support of the view that it is not the old egg which is at fault.

The second, and in some ways simpler, approach is to collect fertilized eggs from the Fallopian tube of an old animal and to transfer them into the uterine environment of a pseudo-pregnant young recipient. The results of such work, carried out in collaboration with Dr. G. B. Talbert (Talbert & Krohn 1966), are given in Table 1 and indicate quite clearly that blastocysts derived from old donors are just as viable as those from a young donor when transferred into a suitable environment. They also show that the young blastocysts fare no better than old ones when transferred to the inhospitable uterine environment of an old host mouse.

The results of both these approaches agree, then, in suggesting that the egg of the aging mouse has not deteriorated. Work by Goodlin (1965) also failed to show any signs of chromosomal abnormalities among the zygotes formed from mating old mice. In addition, none of the 83 offspring derived so far from these old ovarian grafts has shown any abnormalities and all have grown up normally. Some of the sibs have been mated and all their litters have been normal, too.

Table 1. The fate of fertilized mouse eggs (blastocysts) transferred into new uterine environments. (Data from Talbert & Krohn 1966.)

Group Donor/Host	No. of host mice	No. of transferred blastocysts	% implanted at 8 days	% at term
Young/Young	32	163	67	54
Young/Old	38	222	45	25
Old/Young	31	148	68	59

On the other hand, Blaha (1964) has used seemingly identical methods with hamsters which demonstrate that eggs derived from old mothers are much less viable than those from young mothers (Table 2). Finally, one has to recognize the undoubted fact that a particular chromosomal abnormality becomes increasingly common in the oocyte of the human female over 40. This finding is, perhaps, the reflection of an increasing number of chromosomal abnormalities in all sorts of populations of dividing cells with increasing age (Jacobs, Brunton & Brown 1964).

But at least for the mouse, we seem to be tied to the uterus as the proximate cause of failure. Is the failure due to actual use or simply to the passage of time? Ovarian transplantation can again help to differentiate between these possibilities.

In an animal with two uterine horns, one can throw the burden of twice the normal number of foetuses onto one horn by removing one ovary. Compensatory extra ovulations occur in the other remaining ovary and litter size is hardly affected. The number of pregnancies, however, is almost exactly halved (Jones & Krohn 1960: Biggers, Finn & McClaren 1962). When such a stage of failure is reached the mouse can be given a new graft, either to replace the ovary which has supported all the pregnancies or to the other side which has been sterile because the ovary had been removed. This uterine horn will not have been damaged by the physical presence of embryos, though it will have been influenced by the hormonal changes characteristic of pregnancy and might be expected to provide a better milieu for new implants. The results of this sort of experiment are still rather incomplete (Table 3) but they seem to indicate that the unused side is most capable of accommodating new pregnancies, followed by a horn which has had only the normal burden and finally by a horn which has had a double load.

Table 2. The fate of fertilized hamster eggs transferred into new uterine environments. (Data from Blaha 1964.)

Group Donor/Host	No. of hosts	No. of transferred blastocysts	No. of term successes	No. of foetuses	% success
Young/Young	8	63	8	31	49.2
Young/Old	8	72	3	6	8.3
Old/Young	11	88	1	4	4.5

Table 3. Litters from young orthotopic ovarian grafts in old unispayed host mice

Single graft in empty capsule litters		Single graft replacing used ovary litters		Single graft replacing ovary in normal mouse litters	
Before	After[a]	Before	After[a]	Before	After[a]
8	9 + VBs (40:9)	9	4 + VB (12:0)	12	5 + VB (11:3)
12	6 + VB (16:1)	13	7 Abortions	10	7 + VB (14:0)
11	8 + VB (28:4)	14	5 Abortions	13	1 + VB (1:1)
12	7 + VB (27:0)				
9	8 + Dead (27:2)				

[a] VB = Vaginal bleeding indicating loss of pregnancy. (–:–) = Number born alive:dead.

The problem of what has happened to the uterus remains. Changes with the passage of time in histological appearances and in content of collagen certainly occur. However, the aging process in the uterus, if this can be measured by changes in the amount of collagen, is not accelerated by the extra strain of unilateral pregnancies since the increase in the amount of collagen is the same in the two horns (Finn, Filch & Harkness 1963).

It is possible that all the potential implantation sites in the endometrium are used up, or that the decidual reaction of the endometrium becomes less vigorous with increasing age. We are very ignorant of the factors determining where embryos are to implant, nor indeed do we know the extent to which there is any site specificity.

An additional factor may be the amount of vitamin E available. Deficiency of this vitamin is known to affect smooth muscle and also to result in abortions. There is considerable evidence, too, that supplements of vitamin E or, better still, of wheat germ oil improve the reproductive performance of senescent hamsters (Soderwall & Sahinen 1965) and that the vitamin E requirements increase 11-fold at 43–45 weeks and 67-fold in 59-week old rats compared with the needs of 9–11 week old young adults (Ames & Ludwig 1964). However, my own attempts to improve fertility in failing mice by giving supplements of vitamin E have not been successful, perhaps because the amounts given were not large enough.

TRANSPLANTATION AND AGING OF SKIN

One of the central problems in gerontology is to distinguish between local and general causes of aging, to decide, that is, whether a tissue ages according to its own built-in program or because of changes in its environment. I have indicated already how the technique of transplantation gives one a very flexible and universal method for studying these problems by observing the tissue's behavior in old and young environments.

But before this approach can be of value, a suitable measure of the tissue's activity must be readily available. For reproductive function, the number of oocytes in the ovary or the size and frequency of litters are suitable quantitative measurements. For the skin, an equivalent measure of activity which declines with age is needed so that one can then see whether the activity of the old skin—transferred to the young environment—is restored and vice-versa, whether the activity of young skin is depressed by transfer to the old.

Such a measure is to be found in the oxygen consumption of the thin ear skin put into microrespirometers of the type designed and developed by Cruickshank (1954). As it has turned out, the QO_2 is not a completely satisfactory measure because it is only fully regressive over the first four or five months of life, but it is sufficiently valuable to form the basis for experiments in which pieces of old and young skin have been grafted to new environments. After varying periods of time the grafts can be removed and their activity measured and compared with the activity of the host animal's own skin (Mundy & Krohn 1965).

In each instance (Table 4) the graft tissue retains its own characteristic activity and not that of the new environment, i.e., the QO_2 of old skin remains low in a young environment and that of the young skin high in an old environment. The figures also show that the

Table 4. The oxygen uptake ($\mu l\ O_2$/mg dry wt/hr) of ear skin grafted to old and young hosts. (From Mundy & Krohn 1965.)

Age	Host QO₂ Ear skin[a]	Graft	
		QO₂ Old skin[a]	QO₂ Young skin[a]
Young	3.38 ± 0.16 (13)	2.41 ± 0.19 (16)	3.35 ± 0.18 (16)
Old	1.87 ± 0.06 (9)	2.67 ± 0.22 (15)	3.7 ± 0.22 (15)

[a] Figures are means ± standard error (number of observations).

respiratory rate of the skin, whatever its age, is somewhat stimulated by the act of transplantation. This is not surprising but the figures show, in addition, that the old skin is more responsive and the old environment (or the new granulation tissue derived from the old animal) more stimulating.

In looking over these early experiments I became concerned about the possibility that an uncertain amount of host tissue might be included in the graft tissue when it was removed and that the graft might be damaged by the necessary scraping of its undersurface. The ear skin that had been used was stripped off from the layer of cartilage which is interposed, together with connective tissue, between the inner and outer layers of epidermis.

In a new series of experiments the ear skin and underlying thin sheet of cartilage were transplanted together, the idea being that it would be possible to strip the epidermis off the graft at the required time after grafting and so be satisfied that one was dealing with graft tissue only. The preliminary results were quite unexpected. They showed that the presence of cartilage stimulated oxygen consumption by the graft and so clearly that further study of the phenomenon was called for. A new series extending the duration of the grafts from 6 to 49 days was therefore undertaken (Table 5). New normal control groups without cartilage confirmed the previous finding that the activity of young and old grafts is in accordance with their age and not with the environment, old or young, in which they are placed. However, the groups with added cartilage show that the activity of both old and young skins is stimulated by the presence of the underlying cartilage to levels much higher than normal and remains high for much longer than if the cartilage is lacking. But in addition, the young host now provides an almost uniformly more stimulating environment than the old host (Table 5).

The explanation for this effect is not immediately apparent. Counts of epidermal mitoses certainly show, as one might expect, that more cells are dividing, but it seems difficult to fit the observations into any of Bullough's proposals for a "chalone" which controls mitotic activity in the epidermis. Local damage is said to release the surrounding cells from an inhibitor of mitosis whose activity is also lost if adrenalin is lacking (Bullough, Hewett & Lawrence 1964). It is hard to see how the cartilage could be preventing the access of adrenalin when the blood supply to the epidermis is sufficient to sustain an increased mitotic rate, nor does it seem likely that cartilage contains an "anti-inhibitor."

Table 5. Comparison of oxygen uptake (μl O_2/mg dry wt/hr) of old and young ear skin grafted with and without cartilage to old and young hosts.

Graft duration (days)	Grafts without cartilage				Grafts with cartilage			
	Hosts				Hosts			
	Old		Young		Old		Young	
	Donors		Donors		Donors		Donors	
	Young	Old	Young	Old	Young	Old	Young	Old
7–12	3.5 ± 0.34 (9)	2.7 ± 0.32 (10)	4.1 ± 0.15 (36)	2.4 ± 0.22 (9)	4.5 ± 0.54 (10)	4.1 ± 0.23 (11)	4.6 ± 0.2 (47)	3.6 ± 0.34 (8)
19–24	3.8 ± 0.33 (5)	2.4 ± 0.19 (6)	3.2 ± 0.19 (12)	2.6 ± 0.31 (7)	4.1 ± 0.28 (5)	3.5 ± 0.29 (6)	4.4 ± 0.17 (15)	4.1 ± 0.16 (10)
31–36	2.8 ± 0.18 (5)	2.0 ± 0.26 (5)	3.1 ± 0.32 (7)	2.3 ± 0.22 (5)	3.1 ± 0.04 (5)	2.6 ± 0.15 (5)	3.9 ± 0.27 (7)	3.3 ± 0.35 (5)
43–49	2.4 ± 0.26 (5)	1.9 ± 0.05 (5)	2.5 ± 0.24 (5)	1.8 ± 0.1 (6)	2.5 ± 0.18 (6)	2.6 ± 0.18 (9)	3.3 ± 0.43 (8)	2.4 ± 0.27 (7)

a Figures are means ± standard error (number of observations).

Other workers, however, have established a relationship between the applications of crude cartilage extracts and accelerated wound healing (Prudden, Teneick, Svaha & Frueh 1964; Sabo & Enquist 1965). Thus, the local or general administration of bovine cartilage powder, but not of chrondroitin sulfate, can accelerate wound healing. It may be that the cartilage provides a source of some essential metabolite, perhaps a glucosamine, which assists the epidermis to proliferate.

THE SERIAL TRANSPLANTATION OF SKIN

My last example of the use of transplantation in aging studies was originally stimulated by the central dogma, based on Carrel's experiments with tissue cultures, which purported to show that cultures of fibroblasts were immortal and which, at the time, I accepted. (But see Hayflick 1965 and this Symposium.)

It seemed possible that serial transplantation could be used to discover whether an organized tissue, such as skin, could live indefinitely like the cultures of fibroblasts were thought to or whether its life-span would be restricted. Though there are plenty of incidental hazards to this sort of experiment, all one needs is plenty of patience and an ample supply of inbred mice. The technique is simply the serial transfer of a skin graft from one mouse which has been allowed to get old to a new young one. This mouse in turn ages and the original graft, in due course, is moved to yet another young host.

Work of this sort has been going on for more than 5 years but the long-drawn nature of the experiment means that no more can be done now than to provide a progress report which brings up to date the first report (Krohn 1962). At that time it seemed clear that grafts of old A strain skin failed after an initial period of successful growth in young hosts although young skin could be successfully transferred for much longer periods of time, even onto a mouse which had provided an unsatisfactory site for old skin. On the other hand, old CBA skin was more tolerant of the conditions. Further work has confirmed that old A strain tissue rapidly behaves in an inferior fashion to young skin, but old skin from CBA or CBA $\times$ C_{57}, CBA $\times$ A, and C_{57} $\times$ A hybrids is now seen to be unaffected by a first transplantation.

The first experiments made use of body skin for the grafted tissue, but sometimes it was difficult to identify the boundary between the graft and the host. Tail skin was then substituted and is, indeed, readily distinguishable from the surrounding host body skin. However, it seems to be much more prone to undergo shrinkage and, in turn, it has been replaced by the much thinner ear skin which seems to be altogether the most satisfactory source of material for grafting.

There is no doubt, however, that grafts often gradually become smaller as they are transferred and get old, and one has to control the extent to which this is a nonspecific effect of repeated grafting, even at the extended intervals of time used, rather than a specific effect of increasing age. Using shorter intervals between transfers, young skin rapidly loses vitality and is unable to withstand four transfers at intervals of 28 days or even of 42 days. However, another experiment using young and old grafts transplanted simultaneously to the side of the chest and repeatedly transferred at about 40 day intervals, provides no indication that the old grafts are any less able to withstand the stresses of this treatment than are the young ones.

There is an additional difficulty in interpreting the results which is inherent in the method and which has not yet been satisfactorily resolved. On the one hand, Converse, Filler & Ballantyne (1965), for example, believe that the revascularization of a graft is entirely new and comes from the host. Halber and Billingham (1964), on the other hand, believe that original vessels remain and are linked up with the host's vascular channels. Obviously the total age of at least one vitally important component of a skin graft will be dependent on whichever of these views turns out to be right. Similar considerations probably apply to the question of the re-innervation of the graft.

The present situation for the oldest grafts is set out in Table 6. More recently, a group of 19 donors born between July and November, 1961, have been used to supply skin between 901 and 1120 days old when transplanted onto the first young host. Of these 218 grafts, 14 were technical failures or the hosts died soon after, 26 died at various times with intact grafts, 15 were unsatisfactory, and 163 were healthy when they were removed from the first host, 312–414 days later for transfer to a second host. In turn, 12 of these were technical failures, 6 early failures, 27 unsatisfactory, and 116 were healthy when examined a further 120 days after grafting, i.e., when the total age of the grafts was at least 4 years.

Clearly, the experiments have not continued long enough to establish a clear-cut answer to the original problem. It seems that grafts become progressively somewhat less viable but much of this is due to nonspecific damage and in spite of it some grafts have already achieved an overall chronological age certainly double the maximum

Table 6. The behavior of serial skin transplants

Month and year of birth of original donor	Grafts to Host I	Good grafts	To Host II	Good grafts	To Host III	Good grafts	Total age years and months
2/59	14	13	11	3	3	2	6–8/12
11–12/59	30	30	25	16	13	5	6
7/60	10	10	10	6	1[a]	1	5–4/12
10/60	13	11	10	9	8[a]	6	5
12/60	30	25	23	18	11[a]	7	4–10/12
2/61	26	24	20	20	2[a]	2	4–9/12
Total	123	113	99	72	38[a]	23	

[a] More still to be transferred.

recorded age of any mouse. How much longer they will continue remains to be seen.

What can certainly be said is that so far there has been no sign of cancer developing in any of the grafts. Mice only rarely develop spontaneous skin cancer, but they are very susceptible to carcinogenic agents. Old evidence by Leitch (1923) affirms that old mice are no more susceptible than young ones to the induction of cancer, but it is impossible to convince oneself from the paper that old and not simply adult (which may be no more than 4 or 5 months old) mice were used. Further study of this possibility using both normal and grafted skin seems to be very worthwhile.

The experiments have already shown that skin from old A strain mice seems to be less viable than that from other old mice. This difference in viability may, perhaps, be correlated with the shorter life-span exhibited by this strain and the increased number of mitotic abnormalities they develop in their liver cells with increasing age compared with the C_{57} strain (Crowley & Curtis 1963). In the early limit to viability which is suggested, this strain certainly seems to provide a situation comparable to that described by Hayflick (1965) for tissue cultures. The results could also be accommodated by Walford & Hildemann's (1964) view of a relationship between aging and the development of autoimmunity, but would have to imply that the old tissue acquired new histocompatibility antigens rather than that tolerance was lost. However, the results with the other strains do not yet indicate that there is a limit to their life-span.

References

Ames, S. R. and Ludwig, M. I. (1964). *Fed. Proc., 23,* 291.

Ascheim, P. (1964). *Gerontologia (Basel), 10,* 65–75.

Biggers, J. D., Finn, C. and McClaren, A. (1962). *J. Reprod. Fertil., 3,* 303–312.

Blaha, G. C. (1964). *Anat. Rec., 150,* 413–416.

Bullough, W. S., Hewett, C. L. and Lawrence, E. B. (1964). *Exp. Cell Res., 36,* 192–200.

Converse, J. M., Filler, M. and Ballantyne, D. L., Jr. (1965). *Transplantation, 3,* 22–27.

Crowley, C. and Curtis, H. J. (1963). *Proc. Nat. Acad. Sci. U.S.A., 49,* 626–628.

Cruickshank, C. N. D. (1954). *Exp. Cell Res., 7,* 374–380.

DeOme, K. B. (1965). Cited in Hayflick, L., *Exp. Cell Res., 37,* 614–636.

Finn, C. A., Filch, S. M. and Harkness, R. C. (1963). *J. Reprod. Fertil., 6,* 405–407.

Foà, C. (1900). *Arch. Ital. Biol., 34,* 43–73.

Foà, C. (1901). *Arch. Ital. Biol., 35,* 364–372.

Franks, L. M. and Chesterman, F. C. (1964). *Nature (London), 202,* 821.

Geiringer, E. (1956). *J. Geront., 11,* 8.

Goodlin, R. C. (1965). *J. Reprod. Fertil., 9,* 355–356.

Halber, J. A. and Billingham, R. E. (1964). In *Advances in the Biology of Skin,* Montagna, W. R. and Billingham, R. E., Eds., Vol. 5, Pergamon Press, London, p. 165–172.

Hayflick, L. (1965). *Exp. Cell Res., 37,* 614–636.

Jacobs, P. A., Brunton, M. and Brown, W. M. C. (1964). *Ann. Hum. Genet., 27,* 353–365.

Jones, E. C. and Krohn, P. L. (1960). *J. Endocr., 20,* 129–134.

Krohn, P. L. (1962). *Proc. Roy. Soc., B157,* 128–147.

Krohn, P. L. (1964). *Proceedings 5th International Congress for Animal Reproduction and Artificial Fertilization,* Section II, p. 23–55.

Krohn, P. L. (1965). *Brit. Med. Bull., 21,* 157–162.

Leitch, A. (1923). *Brit. Med. J., ii,* 1–7.

Mawdsley, R. and Harrison, G. A. (1963). *J. Embryol. Exp. Morph., 11,* 537–547.

Mundy, J. and Krohn, P. L. (1965). *Gerontologia (Basel), 11,* 45–56.

Pepper, F. J. (1961a). *J. Endocr., 22,* 335–348.

Pepper, F. J. (1961b). *J. Endocr., 22,* 349–360.

Prudden, J. F., Teneick, M. L., Svaha, D. and Frueh, B. (1964). *J. Surg. Res., 4,* 143–144.

Sabo, J. C. and Enquist, I. F. (1965). *Arch. Surg., 91,* 523–525.

Soderwall, A. L. and Sahinen, F. M. (1965). *Fed. Proc., 23,* 466.

Talbert, G. B. and Krohn, P. L., (1966). *J. Reprod. Fertil., 11,* 399–406.

Walford, R. L. and Hildemann, W. H. (1964). *Transplantation, 2,* 87–115.

DISCUSSION

DR. ROCKSTEIN: Another level at which there may be a difference between old and young animals is at the anterior pituitary level where, in an older animal, the feedback mechanism between ovary and pituitary may become disturbed.

DR. KROHN: The whole process of ovulation and the morphological appearance of the developing and formed corpus luteum seem to be entirely normal in the old animals whether they carry a young or an old graft. It is still possible that the old corpus luteum is functionally inadequate, but there is no evidence that this is so. On the other hand, there is some evidence in rats which suggests there is a failure of the hypothalamic-pituitary relations but this does not seem to apply to the mouse.

DR. BRONOWSKI: How do you define "much more likely" when considering the incidence of Mongolism?

DR. KROHN: Much more likely than in a younger mother. It goes from about one in several thousand in the youngest mothers to about 1% or more in the oldest. The figures given by Penrose (*Ann. N.Y. Acad. Sci.* 1954. *57*, 494–502) are:

Age	% Mongols
30–34	0.11
35–39	0.33
40–44	1.24
45–	3.12

DR. BRONOWSKI: You spoke as if some humans at this stage were producing almost 100% of what might be called bad eggs.

DR. KROHN: No, very clearly not. Simply there is a big increase in the proportion of bad eggs in which there is nondisjunction during meiosis.

DR. MEDAWAR: The criterion of normality is very much more exacting in human beings. How do you know that some of the young mice from these old eggs would not be mongoloid? You cannot really rule out that they are abnormal in some way which you would certainly identify and call attention to in human beings.

DR. KROHN: One can only say that all the offspring derived from old eggs, which would normally never have reached maturity if they had stayed in the old environment, appear to be perfectly normal. They have grown up normally. There have been no overt abnormalities, and the offspring from mating them together have also been entirely normal.

Admittedly one has never seen a mongol mouse. However, if human data can be applied to mice one would find only a small percentage affected and these might be missed. It is also true that squash preparations of blastocysts derived from normal mothers, which Goodlin has done, do not show any chromosomal abnormalities. His method is good enough to pick up abnormalities in blastocysts if the ovaries have been irradiated. Of course, the absolute age of the oldest mouse egg is only 2 or 3 whereas the human egg is 40 or 45 years. Small oocytes are usually thought to be metabolically inactive so perhaps a length of time greater than the life-span of a mouse is required for the ovarian changes to develop.

DR. KOHN: Have you tried delaying breeding? Old animals which had not had many litters would test the theory that the actual number of litters, or implantations, is important.

DR. KROHN: This approach runs into complications because mice left un-mated for a long time are less able to conceive when at last they are mated. The normal pituitary-ovarian relationships are interfered with by constantly recurring oestrous cycles, uninterrupted by cycles of pregnancy and lactation.

DR. STRONG: Dr. Roman delayed putting the sexes together. When older mice had their first litter they behaved as if they had 8 or 10 litters (Roman, L. and Strong, L. C. 1962. *J. Geront.*, *17*, 37–39).

DR. KROHN: I think there are two uterine components here. One is directly related to the age of the uterus, irrespective of its breeding ex-perience, but there is clearly another component which depends on the amount of work that has to be done by the uterine horn.

DR. KOHN: In the human there is a great deal of arteriosclerosis of the uterine vessels with increasing age so that the blood supply to the uterus is obviously very much decreased. Has a similar study been carried out in mice?

DR. KROHN: Only orthodox histological studies have been done. Nobody has made any real attempt to measure the blood flow through the uterus. There are changes in collagen and one might imagine that there is more capillary fibrosis. In pigs for instance (and in rats, too), it is certainly true that the uterine vessels become arteriosclerotic, but unfortunately the pigs seem to go on to produce normal-sized litters for a very long time indeed.

DR. BRONOWSKI: How reliable are those figures about the hamster egg transfers?

DR. KROHN: One has the statement that of so many eggs only 4% or 5% were recovered at the end of pregnancy. The number is clearly big enough to say that 4 out of 88 is significantly different from 31 out of 63, which was the situation in the young to young transfers. I have no reason to suppose that the technical competence of the two separate parts of the experiments was any different, and therefore, I think they have to be taken entirely at their face value.

DR. BRONOWSKI: They trouble me because they are wholly at variance with carefully established findings of yours.

DR. KROHN: I am not too worried about this. The hamster is very different from the mouse in many respects and I would be prepared to believe that, in the old hamster egg, the process which we see beginning in the human egg has proceeded further. Clearly, one ought to study old hamster blastocysts more closely and see how many abnormalities there are in them. This sort of work which has been done by Goodlin for the mouse has not been done for the hamster, and should be done.

DR. MEDAWAR: What kinds of explanations are there for the disappearance of oocytes in an exponential fashion, which suggests that they have been lost from accidental causes of random incidence? Yet this cannot be so because there is obviously a systematic element as well.

DR. KROHN: It is just accepted as if it were an act of God at the moment. It was in an attempt to find out whether one could identify any factor which might be responsible that we hypophysectomized mice (Jones, E. C. and Krohn, P. L. 1961. *J. Endocrin.*, *21*, 497–509). There is no doubt that hypophysectomy removes a large component of the process of atresia but some loss continues even in the absence of the pituitary.

DR. MEDAWAR: Does this mean that one rate of exponential loss is replaced by another and lesser rate of exponential loss?

DR. KROHN: Yes.

DR. STREHLER: Is the number lost independent of whether the animals have been repeatedly pregnant?

DR. KROHN: Yes.

DR. STREHLER: Is it possible that after the oocytes get to a certain level of development a few of them that go on further essentially inhibit what the others can do and leave them past a point of no return as far as maturing in a succeeding cycle?

DR. KROHN: There are two processes at work and two times in the development of the oocytes when they may run into trouble. An oocyte may get destroyed early or during the primordial stage and this process is active long before sexual maturity. Subsequently, a proportion of those oocytes which are chosen, whatever that means, to go through the final stages of growth will fall by the wayside before they are actually ovulated. That is a separate process of atresia from the process of destruction of large numbers of the small ones.

DR. GLASER: An exponential law would also be found if there were overcrowding and competition in such a way that the rate at which eggs die is proportional to the number that are there.

DR. KROHN: Some importance may attach to the distance of a follicle from some particular size blood vessel which determines the likelihood that one follicle will be provided with gonadotrophins or other blood borne factors before the next one.

DR. BOURNE: You anticipated me in suggesting that the loss of the early eggs might possibly be due to their relationship to the vascular supply. Might the loss of preovulatory follicles be a mechanical process in which they swell up to a certain point when the surrounding connective tissue resists any further expansion and they give up and die? To what extent are the preovulatory follicles at the surface where you might expect this factor to operate least?

DR. KROHN: I do not know. Clearly if an egg does not get to the surface, it is not going to be able to ovulate. If a preovulatory follicle does not ovulate, it is going to die.

DR. CURTIS: I understand that hypophysectomy decreases this rate of atresia. Can you increase the rate if you give oestrogens?

DR. KROHN: I have never made actual counts of the number of oocytes in oestrogen-treated mice. It has been done in monkeys where the variation from one monkey to the next is very much larger and where it is much more difficult to decide whether an apparent difference is a real one or not. Prolonged administration of oestrogen certainly destroys oocytes. One might think that oestrogen, by its feedback effects on the pituitary, would produce the equivalent of hypophysectomy and it does stunt the animal's growth. The overriding effect on the ovary, however, is the direct destructive one. At one time we thought that androgen could slow down the rate of atresia too, but it turned out not to be so.

DR. GROSS: Would it not be worth looking at the eggs systematically, to find out whether there are any changes in some particular components, and whether these are intrinsic or extrinsically induced?

DR. KROHN: Yes. Nobody has looked properly at differences in the properties of old and young eggs. The subject is wide open for people to get involved in.

DR. WALFORD: Have you tried to make serial transplants of ovaries containing eggs into hypophysectomized animals? In such animals they might survive for a much longer time.

DR. KROHN: No. There are technical problems because the ovarian capsule in the hypophysectomized animal is so small, but it could be done. The problem is mainly a logistic one of getting together a large enough number of long term surviving hypophysectomized mice. What has been done is to take the ovaries from hypophysectomized animals which, in the CBA strain, for instance, still contain eggs long after all the eggs in normal CBA animals have vanished and transfer them into a normal young mouse. Then you can get perfectly normal offspring from the grafts. These fertilized eggs were chronologically at least twice as old as CBA eggs normally ever are. Whether they are metabolically twice as old is another matter because they have been in the quite different environment of an hypophysectomized mouse all that time.

DR. MEDAWAR: The question has been posed whether or not oocytes themselves age. I am sure that Dr. Strong could tell us what is known about lineages of mice maintained through oocytes of different ages.

DR. STRONG: I am very happy that some of the mice I originated nearly 50 years ago are now being used to such an extent in the field of gerontology. The new strains are being developed on the same principles of hybridization and lineal descent through inbreeding as the old but with a change of emphasis on maternal age selection. The original A, CBA, and C_3H strains were developed from one genetic source through a process of hybridization, mendelian segregation, recombination, and the selection toward the incidence of spontaneous tumors. Hence the A and the C_3H strains, had high susceptibility, whereas the CBA strain was selected for longevity and towards resistance to spontaneous tumors. In my laboratory here the CBA mice live longer than any other strain that I have.

The possibility of a maternal age factor in relation to ovulation stems from a selection towards the age at which a mother has her offspring. In this recent experiment, I have again started through a series of hybridizations and, then, basing selection upon the age of the mother at the time of littering, have produced a new colony of mice, with several separated sublines from a common genetic origin. The offspring produced early in the experiment still showed hybrid biological variability. The later mice obtained from continued inbreeding should now be considered genetically uniform.

In each generation I have selected toward early or intermediate aged mothers or toward advancing old aged mothers, so that through these continued, although separate, periods of inbreeding we have mice that have been descended from mothers less than 100 days of age; we also have other mice descended from 101 to 200, 301 to 400, 401 to 500 day old maternal aged mothers and this selective process goes on generation after generation. I have had a few mice born when the mothers were more than 701 days of age.

One of the most interesting things that is coming out of this experiment in relation to gerontology is the effect on longevity. Mice from the earliest maternal age descent (<100 days) lived an average of 625 days. Mice born to mothers in the prime of life, between 201 and 300 days of life lived on an average of 662 days. The data on longevity of offspring in relation to maternal age are given in Figure 1.

It will be impossible to continue the late maternal age descent from mothers between 701–800 days of life. First, I am not going to live long enough, and second, these mice must be more than 2 years of age before they are continued as breeders for the next generation and are living only for an average of between 350 and 400 days. The 601 to 700 day maternal age class will probably also die out; the 501 to 600 day maternal age class

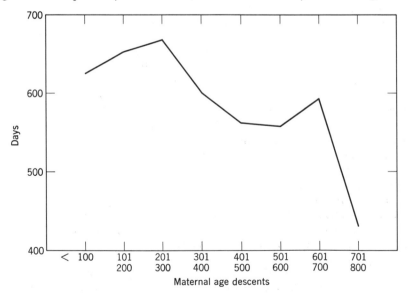

Fig. 1. The longevity of female mice (between F6 and F15) according to maternal age descent.

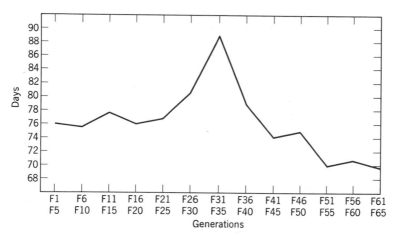

Fig. 2. The age at first litter of the <100 day maternal age descent class according to generations of inbreeding.

is now being continued, but at a very slow rate and I doubt if it will be possible to continue beyond 12 to 14 generations of inbreeding. The <100 day maternal age class has now reached 66 generations of inbreeding, the 101–200 day maternal age class has reached 35 generations of inbreeding, the 201–300 day maternal age class about 26 generations and so on.

When one continues the selection toward early mothers (<100 days) for as long as 66 generations of inbreeding, there is always continued variability beyond what would be expected by the laws of inbreeding. This is true whether the age of first litters, litter frequency, reproductive capacity, longevity, or any other biological characteristic is used as the index. For example, the age of first litters is given in Figure 2. After a low value of 76.0 days for the age of first litters in F_1, the age of the first litters came later and later, the highest value being reached between F_{31}–F_{35}. These later appearing first litters would be expected if the process of inbreeding were producing segregation or recombination of genetic factors involved in the mechanism that determines the age of first litters. After the peak of F_{35} (when they can be considered genetically homozygous) something happened that altered the trend in age of first litters. Variation took place in the direction of selection and the age of first litters came earlier and earlier, until now in F_{65} first litters come earlier than they did when the mice were F_1 hybrids (70.2 days compared to 76.0 days). This is obviously evidence of a mechanism of biological equilibrium; in other words, if you select or if you insult a species too long in one direction a compensatory change takes place which brings the individual back to equilibrium.

DR. MEDAWAR: It would seems that in the experiment you described, two distinct factors are at work. There is (*a*) a genetic factor, when you start with the heterogeneous population, and there is (*b*) the factor related to the age of the oocyte. But now do you have, what I think would be particularly relevant to Professor Krohn's work, data not so much on genetic selection but the choice of young mothers versus old mothers in one inbred strain?

DR. STRONG: There are at least three forces at work. From F_1 to F_{35} one seems to have been dealing with segregation or recombination of genetic factors. Variations took place counter to the trend of selection, i.e., despite selection towards precocious parity litters came later and later. But at F_{35} and after when these mice were assumed to be homozygous, variation took place in the direction of selection. In other words, the maternal age effect is more pronounced on a homozygous condition than on a heterozygous condition. The force of recombination is powerful, but when that force has been reduced to a minimum by long term inbreeding, then an environmental insult, such as maternal age selection, can manifest itself. In addition to the forces of recombination and maternal aging, there is still one other factor involved, the specific gene named LST by Brother Forsthoefel (University of Detroit), who has been interested in the investigation of the embryological effects of this pleomorphic gene. When one reduces "LST" to its recessive form "1st," the biological tempo of change is always reduced. Litters come later, the litter frequency is less, and the mice have fewer tumors.

So far I have not considered the problem of ovulation in reference to the aging process. There is certainly a great volume of unknowns here, too. Such questions as how old is an egg in the ovary before it is released; and does the egg age in the ovary—or not until it is released, need further clarification. I hope to incorporate variations in ovulation as an additional force in my experiment later.

DR. KROHN: The problem here is not so much the actual extent of the total life span of the animal, but its reproductive life-span. If a long-lived animal is capable of reproducing only until 300 days of age then you cannot do anything about any older oocyte; you can have only the effect of the age of a 300 day old oocyte serially transferred by breeding.

DR. MEDAWAR: Even that could be extremely relevant. An intrinsic difficulty of an experiment of this kind is the danger that there will be a cumulative effect of a bad maternal environment and this could be avoided only by alternating old mothers with young mothers as parents of each succeeding generation. Then one would see over a period of time if using old oocytes gave worse results than young oocytes.

The problem is not one of selecting for longevity in a genetically heterogeneous population. We know that this can be done. The problem is whether or not there is any long term cumulative disadvantage in having older as opposed to younger oocytes as the cells which give rise to the next generation. Experiments of this sort have been done in drosophila and rotifers without showing any effect. We need to know what happens in mice.

DR. BOURNE: In some mice where the reproductive life ends much earlier, oestrous cycles continue for quite some time. Could the failure be related to a failure to mate?

DR. KROHN: Only to a slight extent. In the mouse the time of mating is very closely controlled by the hormonal environment, but as the animals get older they do seem to break free of the restrictions to some extent, and certainly in rats they tend to mate outside the optimum time of oestrus. One knows that, if the mating takes place at a distance from the most appropriate time of only a few hours, the chances of normal development are much less.

Transplantation of Skin and Aging

DR. MEDAWAR: From the point of view of aging, what it really amounts to is that in the earlier experiments, using this thickness of skin, you were not measuring quite what you thought you were measuring, but you are still measuring something that is relevant to aging, whatever it may be.

DR. KROHN: Yes. I think the original experiments are valid and that we were gilding the lily in modifying the transplantation technique. What it has done is to introduce the additional problem of explaining the changes in the behavior of grafts brought about by the presence of cartilage.

DR. MEDAWAR: Transplantation of a skin graft is followed by an episode of hyperplasia, which obviously makes special demands on blood supplies. One can well imagine a young environment providing this more quickly or more efficiently than an old one.

DR. KOHN: The change in oxygen uptake is really during the growth period and there is no change between early adulthood and old age. I would submit that you are studying maturation and not aging.

DR. KROHN: On the general notion that whatever one chooses as an aging index has got to decline continuously throughout?

DR. KOHN: It should be obtained after maturity, I would say. You can define aging any way you want.

DR. KROHN: It seems to me that one is justified in making this sort of comparison and using this sort of preparation to see what are the factors which affect the behavior of the skin.

DR. KOHN: You do not have to use animals that live any longer than five or six months for your experiments.

DR. KROHN: That is true, but we have done it in much older mice.

DR. BRONOWSKI: Without cartilage it seems that the graft dictates what happens, and the host does not. With cartilage, however, the host dictates rather than the graft. It seems to me that there is something rather odd about the action of the cartilage being in this direction. Am I not right in thinking that old cartilage is usually supposed to be much less active than young cartilage?

DR. KOHN: Silver proteinate will not diffuse into an old cartilage of a rabbit ear as rapidly as it will in a young cartilage (Stockwell, R. A. and Barnett, C. H., 1964. *Nature, 201,* 835–836). All we know about aging in connective tissue, and collagen in particular, which has a heavy concentration in cartilage, suggests that it is safe to say there are significant differences in aging (Kohn, R. R., in *Reproduction, Molecular, Subcellular, Cellular,* 1965. M. Locke, Ed., Academic Press, New York) .

DR. BRONOWSKI: The old cartilage seems to be more efficient—which is contrary to the way one thinks such things go. I merely want to emphasize that, in the presence of cartilage, the host dominates, in the absence of cartilage the graft dominates. This is exactly the opposite of what I would think to be the case if cartilage in fact played an important part in the reaction.

DR. KROHN: As an example of the extent to which one can manipulate transplantation techniques if one really sets about it, one can now extend this sort of experiment by splitting old skin from old cartilage and young skin from young cartilage and then recombining in old/young sandwiches, which can be placed in old or young environments.

The introduction of cartilage seems to have made the environment more important than it was without it but has not completely removed the old/young differences.

DR. STREHLER: What is the limiting factor in the respiration of the skin, the access of substrate, the amount of mitochondria, the concentration of mitochondrial enzymes, or what? Might not measurements of this sort be done to distinguish one sort of skin from another?

DR. KROHN: This is posing a different question. Because we were not biochemists, we were not asking the question, "Can we determine what are the intimate biochemical differences between old and young cells taken from ear skin?" but, "Are differences that we observe in a particular index of the overall performance of the tissue related to the environment that the tissue finds itself in, or are they concerned with the cells themselves?" The evidence here is that this is something that has to do with the components of the tissue and therefore another step clearly would be to look at the tissue to see what differences one could find that would account for this metabolic difference.

When would people be satisfied that a tissue has been serially propagated long enough for them to believe that it might go on forever?

DR. HAYFLICK: One thing that should be considered before answering is the extent to which normal cell replication is taking place in the parasitic tissue.

DR. KROHN: But you are not visualizing, are you, that the cells in a graft simply placed in a different position on the body surface are going into suspended animation and do not maintain their ordinary activities? They certainly grow hairs normally.

LYSOSOMES AND AGING PIGMENT*

David Brandes

Departments of Pathology,
Baltimore City Hospitals,
and Johns Hopkins University,
School of Medicine,
Baltimore, Maryland

The most widely accepted cellular change which may be related to the aging process consists in the progressive accumulation of lipofuscin granules in certain cells of the body (DeRobertis, Nowinski & Saez 1960; Bondareff 1959; Bourne 1957; Wilcox 1959). These granules have also been called "wear and tear" or aging pigments, apparently derived from the cytoplasm in the process of wasting (Boyd 1953).

One of the best examples is provided by the so-called brown atrophy of the heart, a wasting of the myocardium seen in old age and in cachectic diseases. In light microscopical preparations, the aging pigment appears as an accumulation of brown granules in cardiac muscle and in other tissues such as nerve cells, seminal vesicles, adrenal cortex, corpus luteum, prostate gland, and interstitial cells of the testes.

Very little has been known about the possible significance of the accumulation of aging pigment in the cells of older individuals, especially in vital organs, such as the heart and the central nervous system. More recent studies with the electron microscope, and especially with the application of histochemical techniques at the level of resolution of the electron microscope, have served to gain further insight into the functional significance of these pigment bodies.

There is at present good evidence that the aging pigment may be related to another cellular structure known as the lysosome. According to De Duve (1959a), the lysosomes contain most, if not all, of the cellular enzymes able to break down any substance within the cell.

* The work here reported has been supported by Grant HD 00042-05, National Institute of Child Health and Human Development, National Institutes of Health, U.S. Public Health Service.

149

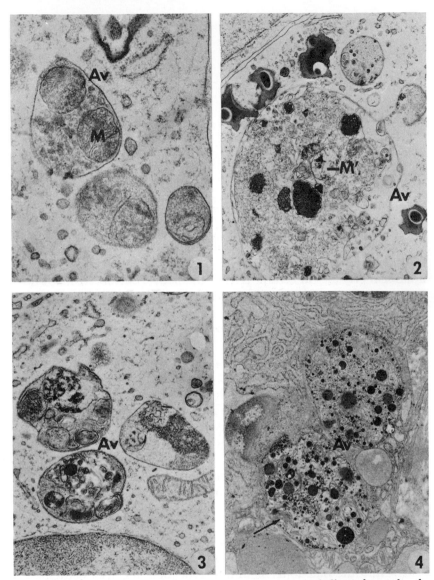

Figs. 1 to 5. Mouse macrophage: Alteration of normal metabolic pathways by the alkylating agent Cytoxan. The various apparent stages by which aging bodies may evolve from autophagic vacuoles. Abbreviations: Av = autophagic vacuoles; M = mitochondria within autophagic vacuoles: M' = mitochondria in process of degradation within autophagic vacuole; N = nucleus; arrows (→) point to myelin figures within autophagic vacuoles or within age pigments: arrow heads (➤) point to lead deposits, indicative of acid phosphatase activity within autophagic vacuoles.

In normal circumstances, the enzymes of the lysosomes appear to be concerned mainly with the breaking down process necessary for providing the cell with new material for building up structural components to maintain basic metabolic processes. The possibility that lysosomes may be concerned with the "breaking up" phase required for the provision of materials necessary for the cell to carry out synthetic processes has also been postulated (De Duve 1959b). In essence, the lysosomes appear in the cells as small bags surrounded by a membrane and contain most of the degradative enzymes. The membrane that surrounds each lysosome prevents these enzymes from acting on the cell structures which would lead to serious alterations, including cell death. Under these circumstances, the lysosomes represent storage granules for powerful lytic enzymes which are maintained in an inactive form. Such lysosomes have therefore been termed "pure" or primary lysosomes.

There is now substantial evidence that the primary lysosomes may become activated under a variety of physiological and pathological conditions and that, under such conditions, portions of a cell or the entire cell may be destroyed.

Work from our laboratory (Brandes, Bertini & Smith 1965) has shown that lysosomes play an important role in physiologic cell death. The fatty material excreted by the sebaceous glands is made up of debris of cells that have been destroyed in the process of secretion. Our studies have shown that, during maturation and production of secretory material the primary lysosomes increase in number and in the last stages appear to release the digestive enzymes into the cytoplasm. This is followed by degenerative changes leading to cell death, and the broken-up material derived from the dead cells becomes incorporated into the secretion. In many respects, this may be compared to a programmed process of accelerated cell death in relation to the entire organism.

Lysosomes appear also to be involved in the involution and cell death found during normal embryogenesis [e.g., the regression of

Fig. 1. Autophagic vacuoles containing ground cytoplasmic materials, mitochondria, and vesicular structures.

Figs. 2 and 3. Degradation of the digestible material within the autophagic vacuoles leads to the gradual disappearance of recognizable organelles.

Fig. 4. The nondigestible lipoproteins tend to become arranged in the form of myelin figures and lipid droplets become abundant. The relation between these autophagic vacuoles and lysosomes is established by the presence of lysosomal hydrolases. The lead deposits, indicative of acid phosphatase activity, are shown in Fig. 5.

tadpoles' tails, the chick Mullerian duct and the mesonephron in mammals (Novikoff 1961)].

The activation of digestive enzymes of the lysosomes in the cell may give rise to the formation of bodies known as secondary or derived lysosomes. One of these, the autophagic vacuole, also referred to as a cytolysome, is of special interest in the study of aging, as it appears to represent an intermediate stage between the primary lysosome and the aging pigment observed in cells of old individuals.

Morphologically, the autophagic vacuole consists of an area of cytoplasm surrounded by a membrane and containing cellular organelles such as mitochondria and endoplasmic reticulum. Almost invariably, the structures contained in the autophagic vacuole show signs of degradation which are attributed to the action of digestive enzymes derived from the primary lysosomes. Autophagic vacuoles have been observed in a large variety of cells during the course of unfavorable metabolic events in their life cycle. A few examples of work performed in our laboratory and reports published by other investigators will serve to clarify this point.

Brandes, Buetow & Bertini (1964) have shown in a study on the effect of starvation on the unicellular organism Euglena that portions of the cytoplasm, including mitochondria, become encapsulated within membrane bound bodies or autophagic vacuoles. Progressive degradation of the encapsulated material may represent a mechanism for providing the cell with breakdown products for ultilization in continued maintenance of basic metabolic processes in the presence of a hostile environment. Autophagic vacuoles have also been observed in the liver of starved rats (De Duve 1963), and this phenomenon has been interpreted as constituting a mechanism which enables the cells to feed on their own substance without irreparably damaging the entire cell.

The formation of autophagic vacuoles or related bodies has been observed in a variety of pathological conditions resulting from the blockage of, or interference with, normal metabolic pathways by agents such as X-rays, alkylating agents (Brandes & Anton 1966); and in prostatic cells after hormonal deprivation (Brandes 1966). Most of the material within the autophagic vacuoles is digested by the lysosomal enzymes, except for some lipoprotein complexes. At this stage, the hydrolytic enzymes within the lysosomes tend to disappear, and part of the cell body remains occupied by vacuoles loaded with nondigestible material. These structures have been termed "residual bodies," and are indistinguishable from the aging pigment.

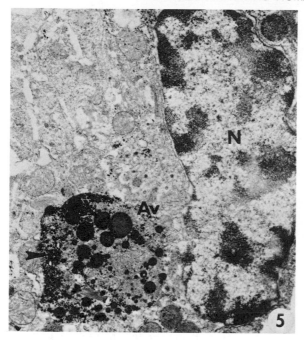

Fig. 5. Through gradual disappearance of hydrolytic enzymes, the autophagic vacuoles assume the morphological characteristics of residual bodies, which are indistinguishable from the age pigment as seen in many organs.

A common denominator has been found in our studies which can be summarized as follows: When cells are subjected to unfavorable metabolic conditions, they resort to the autophagic mechanism which enables them to digest portions of their own cytoplasm, presumably for reutilization in basic metabolic processes. It seems, however, that the lysosomal enzymes incorporated within the autophagic vacuoles are deficient in lipolytic enzymes and that lipid digestion remains incomplete within these bodies, giving rise to residual bodies or aging pigment. De Duve (1964) has suggested that the accumulation of lipid residues which takes place during the process of aging may result from the poor lipolytic activity of lysosomes. It appears that in the lower species the residual bodies derived from autophagic vacuoles which have used up their digestive enzymes can be eliminated, and this process has been referred to as cellular defecation. Higher organisms appear to have lost their ability to eliminate unwanted cellular residues, and the end result seems to be the accumulation of residual bodies or aging pigment. This has been attributed to

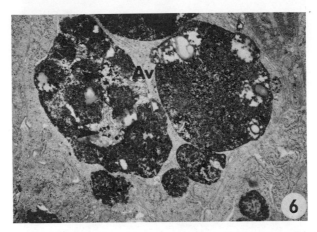

Figs. 6 to 8. Prostatic epithelial cells. Abbreviations: Av = autophagic vacuoles; Ap = age pigment; M = mitochondria within autophagic vacuoles; arrows ($\longrightarrow$) point to myelin figures within autophagic vacuoles or age pigments, arrow heads (➤) point to lead deposits, indicative of acid phosphatase activity within autophagic vacuoles.

Fig. 6. Removal of androgenic stimulus (castration) leads to the accumulation of autophagic vacuoles in the epithelium of the rat prostate. The bodies contain lipid material and myelin figures. The lead deposits indicate the presence of lysosomal enzymes (acid phosphatase). The mechanism of metabolic inhibition in this case is represented by deprivation of a specific hormonal stimulus (androgens), which is normally necessary for protein synthesis in these cells (William-Ashman 1964).

a process of cellular "constipation" in the course of evolution reflected in the inability of cells from higher organisms to get rid of waste material (De Duve 1964).

Strehler, Mark, Mildvan & Gee (1959) have shown quantitatively that aging pigment (lipofuscin) accumulates with age in the human myocardium. These authors have postulated that "because of its absence in the very young, its presence without exception in the aged hearts, its lack of correlation with specific cardiac disease or heart failure, and its large displacement of myocardial volume, the accumulation of lipofuscin in the human myocardium seems to meet the criteria set forth for a basic biological aging process."

In the following paragraphs an attempt will be made to fit the above concepts into a tentative generalization intended to establish a relationship between lysosomes and aging pigment. The latter bodies, because of their physical displacement of cellular volume in vital organs, such as the heart and central nervous system, may be responsible for the loss of function of such cells.

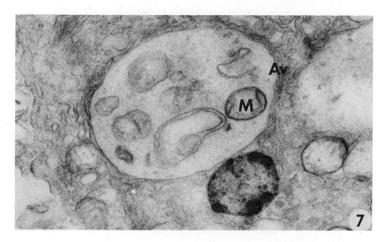

Fig. 7. Autophagic vacuoles can also be seen in prostatic epithelium of older individuals and, by comparison with the findings in rats, the possibility that their presence in the cells reflects a decrease of androgenic stimulus with age may be suggested.

The formation of intracellular bodies similar to aging pigment can be rapidly induced in young subjects by agents or procedures which block normal biosynthetic pathways (X-rays, antimetabolites, starvation, hormonal deprivation). Similar results can be obtained by blocking bioenergetic pathways (loss of ATP, loss of enzymes, etc.). In many respects this may then be considered as an accelerated aging, and normal aging of the cells may be related to similar processes which act, however, at a minimal rate during a prolonged period of time.

The aging pigment seen in older individuals may be derived from autophagic vacuoles in which incomplete digestion due to a deficiency of lipolytic enzymes has caused the accumulation of lipid residues. Their accumulation in the cells may be further due to the loss of the cellular defecation mechanism present in lower organisms.

Taking into account the above pathogenic speculations, therapeutic attempts fall into several categories:

1. Restoration of the cellular defecation mechanism lost during evolution.

2. If the progressive accumulation of lipid residues in the course of aging is due to the poor lipolytic activity of the lysosomes, the possibility of instituting enzymatic replacement therapy should be considered. Many substances, when given parenterally, are known to end up within lysosomes, and it may therefore be possible to

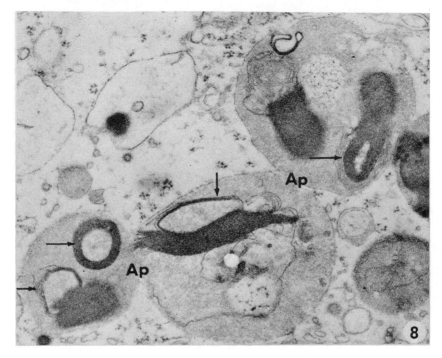

Fig. 8. Prostatic cells from old individuals also show numerous bodies with the ultrastructural characteristics of age pigment. The possibility that they derive from autophagic vacuoles provides an attractive argument in establishing the relationship between lysosomes, autophagic vacuoles and age pigment.

More evidence than that shown here on the basis of conveniently arranged electron micrographs will be required to prove conclusively such relationship as mentioned above.

couple lipolytic enzymes to such substances in the hope that they may become incorporated within the lysosomes and help to digest the lipid residues.

Recent studies (Brandes & Anton 1966) have shown that primary and secondary lysosomes, such as autophagic vacuoles which seem to represent precursors of aging pigment, may be acted upon by substances known as lysosomal labilizers and stabilizers. It is conceivable then that such substances may act upon the aging pigment or their precursors.

3. Institution of prophylactic measures to counteract the aging-dependent decline of biologic activities which seem to result in a relative blockage of normal metabolic pathways, leading to autophagia and the accumulation of undigestible cellular residues.

References

Bondareff, W. (1959). In *Handbook of Aging and the Individual,* J. E. Birren, Ed., Univ. of Chicago Press, Chicago, p. 136–172.

Bourne, G. H. (1957). In *Modern Trends in Geriatrics,* W. Hobson, Ed., Hoeber, New York, p. 22–49.

Boyd, W. (1953). In *A Textbook of Pathology,* Lea and Febinger, Philadelphia, p. 35.

Brandes, D. (1966). *Int. Rev. Cytol., 20,* 207–276.

Brandes, D. and Anton, E., (1966). *Lab. Invest., 15,* 987–1006.

Brandes, D., Bertini, F. and Smith, E. W. (1965). *Exp. and Molec. Path., 4,* 245–265.

Brandes, D., Buetow, D. E. and Bertini, F. (1964). *Exp. and Molec. Path., 3,* 583–609.

De Duve, C. (1959a). In *Subcellular Particles,* T. Hayashi, Ed., Ronald, New York, p. 128.

De Duve, C. (1959b). *Exp. Cell Res.,* Suppl. 7, 169.

De Duve, C. (1963). *Sci. Amer., 208,* 64–72.

De Duve, C. (1964). *Fed. Proc.,* 23:5, 1045.

DeRobertis, E. D. P., Nowinski, W. W. and Saez, F. A. (1960). In *General Cytology,* 3rd ed., Saunders, Philadelphia, p. 555.

Novikoff, A. B. (1961). In *The Cell,* Vol. 2, J. Brachet and A. Mirsky, Eds., Academic Press, New York, p. 423–488.

Strehler, B. L., Mark, D. D., Mildvan, A. S. and Gee, M. V. (1959). *J. Geront., 14,* 430–439.

Wilcox, H. H. (1959). In *The Process of Aging in the Nervous System,* J. E. Birren and W. F. Windle, Eds., C. C Thomas, Springfield, Illinois, p. 16–23.

William-Ashman, H. G. (1964). In *Cellular Control Mechanisms and Cancer,* Elsevier, Amsterdam, p. 104.

DISCUSSION

DR. TILL: This seems to me mainly a problem of garbage disposal. It is an effect, not a cause.

DR. STREHLER: The pigment accumulates linearly with time in human myocardium at about 0.3% per decade (Strehler, B. L., Mark, D., Mildvan, A. S. & Gee, M., 1959. *J. Geront., 14,* 430–439). There is no acceleration of the accumulation in later life. The central problem is to determine what the effect of this accumulation is on the function of individual cells.

DR. KOHN: Dr. Strehler, I believe, has attempted this sort of correlation but found no association between the efficiency of function of the heart and the amount of pigment which had accumulated.

DR. STREHLER: That is right, there was no correlation with any specific disease. As far as neural function is concerned, again one knows that the amount of pigment increases with time and that neuro-function decreases in certain respects with time, but that does not say that the one is the cause of the other.

DR. BOURNE: The granules accumulate to such an extent in the heart muscle as to suggest mechanical interference with the functioning of the fiber. Even though, as Dr. Strehler says, they are not specifically associated with any particular heart disease, the myocardium could still become inefficient because of the accumulation of garbage.

DR. ORGEL: Is the accumulation of pigment by an individual correlated with his performance?

DR. STREHLER: This is the kind of experiment that needs to be done, the problem is how to do it.

DR. KOHN: What cytoplasmic constituents do these lysosomes break down? You mentioned that there are enzymes there which can digest all the cytoplasmic components, but the studies, of which I am aware, report that, while there are enzymes which can degrade some components of the mitochondria (Sawant, P. L., Desai, I. D. & Tappel, A. L. 1964, *Biochim., Biophys. Acta, 85,* 93–102), other components of the cytoplasm resist digestion. Skeletal muscle accumulates lipofuscin granules conspicuously, but we have been unable to isolate any granule associated protease which is capable of degrading the major structural proteins in muscle such as myosin. So I would question that these bodies can really eat up all cell constituents.

CELL DEATH IN EMBRYOS:
ACCELERATED SENESCENCE?

J. W. Saunders, Jr.*

Department of Biology,
Marquette University,
Milwaukee, Wisconsin

We have recognized that, whereas aging leads to death, the chronological aspect of aging must be distinguished from senescent change. The former clearly begins at fertilization; but does senescent change likewise begin at that time or during embryogenesis?

Death is a prominent feature of early development; for example, cataclysmic degeneration eliminates the entire tail of the frog tadpole during metamorphosis, and larval tissues of the holometabolous insect degenerate rapidly after pupation. Death of cells in these systems occurs in response to the hormones of metamorphosis, and thus can hardly be considered as resulting from an accelerated senescence imposed embryonically. Indeed, in the absence of appropriate hormone, the larval cells survive essentially indefinitely. But early cell deaths are also associated with a great many morphogenetic and histogenetic processes. Dr. Krohn has called our attention to the dramatic degeneration of oocytes at the time of birth in the mammal. Even earlier, the primordial germ cells are, reportedly, reduced in number by death during normal development, and are reduced even more extensively in certain mutant conditions (Mintz 1960).

In embryonic stages of the chicken, the sculpturing of the appendages is accompanied by waves of massive degeneration which sweep along the pre- and post-axial margins of the limb bud; this process culminates in the elimination by death of interdigital tissues as the contours of the fingers and toes emerge.

Histogenetic and morphogenetic deaths of these kinds conceivably could result from an accelerated program of senescent change in the cells concerned. Indeed, the suggestion that this is so is frequently

---

* Present address: School of Veterinary Medicine, University of Pennsylvania, Philadelphia, Pennsylvania.

made to me during discussions of our work on embryonic cell death, and it might be worthwhile, therefore, to examine this possibility. I shall do so, however, without attempting to restate or improve on definitions of senescence offered during earlier papers. Suffice it to say, that if premature senescence is programmed into these cells, they might very well proceed to death independently of their normal environment and at very early stages begin to show progressive signs of their forthcoming demise.

To examine this question let us turn our attention to the posterior junction of wing bud and body wall in the chick embryo where, at stage 24 (Hamburger & Hamilton 1951, stage seriation; four days of incubation), a zone of intense necrosis is evident. In embryos supravitally stained with Nile Blue Sulfate or Neutral Red, or in fixed preparations variously stained, this zone is seen to comprise masses of cellular debris, mostly ingested by macrophages. A little debris may be found here at stage 23, a few hours earlier, but essentially none at younger limb bud stages.

Death is programmed for the cells of this "Posterior Necrotic Zone" (PNZ) at state 17 (slightly less than 3 days of incubation), the earliest stage prior to degeneration that the zone can be identified with certainty. If the PNZ be excised from embryos in stages 17 through 23 and grafted to the somite region of the same or another embryo, cataclysmic necrosis is observed in the graft on schedule at stage 24 (of the donor!). Other limb-bud cells grafted to this region do not show necrosis. Thus there is a kind of "death clock" operating in the PNZ cells as early as stage 17 (Saunders, Gasseling & Saunders 1963). Is this clock ticking off a program of senescent change?

Apparently not! Observations with the light microscope and the electron microscope have not yet revealed distinctive changes, much less any which could be characterized as "senescent," in the PNZ area even as late as stage 22. PNZ cells prior to this stage, even though programmed for death, are still vigorous, healthy cells which may yet follow a developmental pathway other than death; for, if PNZ tissues from embryos of stages 17 through 21 are grafted to the dorsal side of the same or a different host wing bud, necrosis fails to occur, and the graft may differentiate extra cartilage, skin, and feather germs (Saunders, Gasseling & Saunders 1963).

Some indications are that the cells whose debris is found in macrophages at stage 24 actually were morbid at stage 22. If the embryo be pulsed with tritiated thymidine prior to stage 22 and fixed at stage 24, a high percentage of degenerating nuclei show radioactivity in autographs. Very few show label, however, if the pulse be administered at stage 22, or later (Held and Saunders 1965). Thus DNA synthesis may be turned off at this stage. We are now seeking to determine whether the pattern of RNA readout changes at this time. M. Ricklin, using the electron microscope in my laboratory, finds in the PNZ at stage 22 some distinctive cells with increased electron density in the nucleus, and "decayed" polysomes. These may be the morbid cells, but one is not yet certain.

Macrophages are not recognized in the PNZ area until cells are actually being ingested. Only at that time, too, does the histochemically demonstrative activity of acid phosphatase increase in the PNZ. This suggests that neighbors of the morbid cells cannibalize them and then synthesize lysosomal enzymes used in hydrolysis of the debris.

In sum, the analysis of morphogenetic death in the wing bud suggests that it is not the consequence of an accelerated program of senescent change. Rather it is the programmed "suicide" of healthy cells triggered by some yet unknown factors of the microenvironment.

References

Hamburger, V. and Hamilton, H. L. (1951). *J. Morphol., 88,* 49–92.
Held, W. and Saunders, J. W. (1965). *Amer. Zool., 5,* 214 (abstr.).
Mintz, B. (1960). *J. Cell. and Comp. Physiol., 56* Supp. 1, 31–48.
Saunders, J. W., Gasseling, M. T. and Saunders, L. C. (1963). *Develop. Biol., 5,* 147–178.

DISCUSSION

DR. MEDAWAR: There are some examples of a programmed death in embryonic life, like the involution of the mesonephros in the developing chick, where perhaps lymphocytes have something to do with the process and where changes akin to those of an auto-immune reaction occur. Does anything of the kind occur here?

DR. SAUNDERS: Not to my knowledge. I have not been able to find good accounts of the regression of the mesonephros. Several old papers that I read did not help much, and the sections we have made have not been very informative.

DR. MEDAWAR: You speak of these cells dying, but one's first instinct is to think that they are killed. If they are killed by some external agency it would not occur to anyone to think that senescent changes had occurred.

DR. SAUNDERS: But people do think so; they ask about this; that is why I posed the question as I did. I wanted to lay to rest the notion that these morphogenetic deaths are the consequence of senescence.

DR. GROBSTEIN: Is there anything in the sequence of events that is different from any typical differentiation of new cell types?

DR. SAUNDERS: I would like to think of this as a case in which death is the end point of differentiation. Death is thus a morphogenetic event which is just as positive, let us say, as the induction of a feather.

You may be interested to know that if we make a millipore filter assembly *in vitro* with dorsal wing tissue on one side and young PNZ tissue on the other, some factor will move through the filter and save the PNZ from death. Somite tissue will not provide this factor [Fallon, J. F. & Saunders, J. W. (1965). *Amer. Zool.*, *5*, 213–214 (abstr.)].

GENERALIZING BIOLOGIC HYPOTHESES
AND AGING: AN IMMUNOLOGICAL APPROACH*

Roy L. Walford

Department of Pathology,
University of California School of Medicine,
Los Angeles, California

Comfort has remarked that modern immunology may be considered a "growth stock," and that it is worth reconsidering many of the unsolved problems of biology in terms of this rapidly advancing discipline (Comfort 1963). Before briefly undertaking such a task in relation to aging, I should like to emphasize that any generalizing biologic hypothesis, such as the various theories of aging currently in vogue, must squarely face *all* the *pertinent* facts and experimental observations. Theories of aging which have been promulgated consequent to preoccupation with age changes in collagen, with certain biochemical parameters, cells in tissue culture, and with irradiation experiments—to name only a few samples—must also be able to account for important observations about aging from more or less unrelated fields of inquiry. The literature of biology is so vast that by an appropriately biased (albeit unintentional) selection of facts, one could find support for any reasonable hypothesis. This tendency must be guarded against. The various observations and experimental results related to gerontology can be divided into those which are highly pertinent, i.e., which a theory cannot fail to come to grips with if it is to be regarded as plausible, and those which in relation to the theory are merely neutral observations. For example, underfeeding during childhood significantly prolongs life-span in many animals (McCay 1952; Fanestil & Barrow 1965), and no aging theory can be retained which fails to encompass this observation. The concentrations of certain enzymes in the liver show mild to moderate alterations with age. At present these may be classified as neutral findings.

* Supported by U.S. Public Health Research Grant No. HD-00534.

163

Table 1 is an attempt in outline form to juxtapose several of the current theories of aging with some of the major, pertinent gerontologic observations. It is an illustrative, not an exhaustive listing. Also the applicability of a few of these observations is open to question. Whether irradiation really accelerates "physiologic" aging or shortens life-span due to other causes is as yet unsettled. Nevertheless one must consider the results of irradiation experiments in a provisional manner until conclusive evidence one way or the other is presented. Table 1 states in a number of cases whether, in terms of each theory, the experimental facts are explicable, whether they cannot be encompassed, or whether they may for the present be regarded as "neutral" in relation to the theory. These interpretations are of course subject to disagreement, and I have left many spaces blank.

The immunologic theory of aging, as I see it, postulates that aging is intimately related to long-term, minor-grade histo-incompatibility reactions among the body's populations of cells (Walford 1962, 1964). These reactions might follow somatic mutation, particularly of lymphoid cells, or loss of homeostatic mechanisms governing tolerance for "self." The primary cause is not critical to the hypothesis, which concerns pathogenesis rather than etiology. A somatic mutation approach is envisaged in Figure 1. Mutation to the D_2 cell (Figure 1) would yield a daughter cell not recognized by the host as being foreign, but the cell would itself recognize the host as being foreign. The daughter cell might then react against the host according to the usual transplantation disease mechanisms.

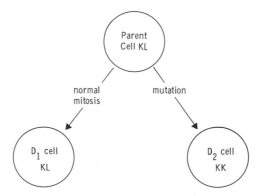

Fig. 1. Heuristic model of somatic mutation of histocompatibility gene L into K, as shown in D_2 daughter cell. Note that D_2 is not a biochemically abnormal cell. KK is just as normal as KL, analogous to any erythrocyte of blood group AA compared to AB. However, in this particular host environment, D_2 would recognize the L gene of the parent (host) as "foreign."

Table 1. A comparative juxtaposition of five theories of aging with pertinent gerontologic observations

Aging theory	Effect of Temperature on life-span	Linear decline in physiologic parameters vs. exponential rise in mortality rates with age	Changes in collagen and DNA with age	Effect of irradiation on life-span	Accumulation of age pigment	Chemical and immunologic status with age	Effect of diet on life-span	Longer life-span of females	All living things age
Crosslinking theory: that large polymers (DNA, collagen, etc) undergo crosslinkage with age	No data available	—	Excellent correlation	X-ray a strong crosslinking agent; but work with radiomimetic drugs, and irradiated insects, does not support the theory	—	Poor correlation	Good correlation	—	Applicable
Denaturation theory: that those protein and other molecules which are not turned over metabolically undergo a slow thermal denaturation	Negative evidence from drosophila	—	—	Large doses can denature biochemically active molecules	—	Poor correlation	—	—	Applicable
Clinker theory: aging is due to the accumulation of insoluble by-products of metabolism	No data available	—	—	—	Excellent correlation	Poor correlation	Good correlation	—	Applicable
Somatic mutation: spontaneous mutations lead to defective cells	Heat is mutagenic. Negative drosophila	—	—	X-ray a strong mutagen; but work with radiomimetic drugs, and irradiated insects, tends not to support theory	—	Poor correlation	—	—	Applicable
Immunologic theory: immunogenetic diversification or loss of tolerance affects intercellular relations	Immune response decreases with lowering of temperature	—	—	Probable good condition if consider opposing effects	—	Good correlation	Possible correlation	Possible correlation	Cannot explain

Let us now inquire which of the major facts of aging (provisional or otherwise) can be interpreted in immunologic terms. Poikilothermic vertebrates, such as fish, show a very considerable increase in life-span when maintained at a lower as compared to a higher temperature. This increase is not due simply to slowing down of metabolism, for growth rates and eventual adult size may actually be accelerated by the reduced temperature (Liu & Walford 1966). The homograft immune response, however, is definitely temperature dependent. Scale grafts in goldfish display quite prolonged survivals in a colder environment (Hildemann 1957). Increased life-span under these conditions is thus explicable in immunologic terms.

Irradiation in small to moderate doses (for example, 400 r to small rodents) shortens the life-span of vertebrates. It is quite uncertain whether this effect represents true physiologic aging or other factors. Some "diseases of aging," such as senile amyloidosis in hamsters (Walford, Sjaarda & Anderson 1965), are seen at a younger age in irradiated than in normal animals, but the incidence of other "aging" diseases—for example, hepatomas in mice (Connell & Alexander 1959)—is not similarly affected. Certain chemical parameters of normal aging, including changes in collagen, are not affected by irradiation (Walford et al. 1965; Dardeu & Upton 1964), nor is renal lysozyme elevated by this treatment (Troup, Wagner & Walford 1965). This is obviously not an area of inquiry that can be settled or even elaborated upon at length in the present discussion. *If* irradiation accelerates true aging, then the following remarks may be pertinent.

Irradiation is a mutagenic agent that should lead to immunogenetic diversification of the body's (lymphoid and other) cells. Such an effect would accord with an immune pathogenesis for aging. But irradiation also *suppresses* the immune response. Thus two opposing effects, one causing immunogenetic diversification and the other inhibiting the immunologic consequences of that diversification, can be envisaged. Some of the seemingly anomalous findings with regard to the effect of irradiation and radiomimetic drugs might be interpretable in terms of such opposing effects. Nitrogen mustard is a radiomimetic drug, but it also powerfully depresses the immune response. It does not cause life shortening (Curtis 1963). Myleran and chlorambucil do shorten life-span (Alexander & Connell 1960) and seem not to be effective as suppressors of immunity.

The results of a preliminary study of the possible effect of the immunosuppressive agent Imuran on the life-span of mice is shown in Figure 2. Sixty-nine 1-year-old mice were divided into three batches of 25, 22, and 22 each. Twenty-five were kept as controls, 22 had 100 mg/kg of Imuran incorporated into their diet, and 22 were on 200 mg of Imuran. The 200 mg level proved to be toxic. At death a number of mice revealed early necrobiosis of the liver. They displayed an accelerated death rate (Figure 2). The mice on the 100 mg Imuran diet, however, demonstrated a mean survival time 10 weeks longer than the controls. This experiment must be repeated, probably with other doses of Imuran and including a declining dosage for progressively older mice. We have noted that if mice about 2 years old are placed on a 100 mg Imuran diet, they actually die at an accelerated rate, resembling the 200 mg level for younger mice (Figure 2).

On the whole, an immunologic interpretation of aging correlates very well with what I have listed in Table 1 as the chemical and immune status with age. Aging is characterized by a surprising lack of demonstrable major chemical alterations. It it true that certain mild to moderate quantitative alterations in liver enzymes have been found, but these are not even great enough to be beyond dispute. Some workers may report a change in a particular enzyme and others not. The only enzyme in mice that shows a striking change with age is one we have recently been working with, and that is renal lysozyme. This increases 4- to 30-fold in advanced age in

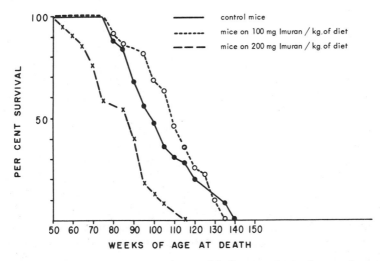

Fig. 2. Effect of dietary supplementation with Imuran, beginning at 1 year of age, on subsequent life-span of (C3H×C57B1) F₁ hybrid mice. Twenty-five control mice and 22 mice on each Imuran regime were followed.

"normal" mice. Furthermore, the increase takes place chiefly during the last third of life in the mouse (Troup, Wagner & Walford 1965). In old hamsters renal lysozyme also increases compared to values for young adult animals (Troup, Wagner & Walford 1965). Now renal lysozyme to a considerable degree reflects immunological activity. It is greatly elevated during hyperimmunization, homologous disease in F_1 hybrids (Suu & Congdon 1964), classical runt disease (Troup, Wagner and Walford 1965), and in certain neoplastic conditions.

Turning now to immunologic parameters (reviewed elsewhere) (Walford 1964), one may note that in apparently normal old humans, i.e., those with no demonstrable disease, the incidence of positive tests for the rheumatoid factor is 16 to 50%, depending upon methodology; antinuclear factors reach an incidence of 13 to 20% with age; antibodies for thyroid tissue and gastric parietal cells increase to about 20%. Gamma-globulin levels are augmented in the serum or normal, aged individuals. These findings may suggest a considerable degree of subclinical auto-immune activity with age.

It has been known since McCay's classic experiments (1952) that underfeeding of vertebrates during the first or growth phase of life markedly prolongs the total life-span. Now the lymphoid apparatus as judged by organ weights, and including the thymus, is markedly sensitive to undernutrition (Walford, in press).

In the vast majority of vertebrates, females enjoy on the average a longer life-span than males. Can this fact be explained immunologically? Perhaps. If one considers those probable auto-immune diseases which are by age-specific incidence also "diseases of aging" (cold-antibody type idiopathic acquired hemolytic anemia, polyarteritis, diabetes mellitus, amyloidosis), one finds a higher incidence in males than in females. In other words, males age faster and have a higher incidence of these types of auto-immune disease (Walford, in press).

Immunologic theory cannot explain aging in animals which do not possess an immunologic system. There is no convincing evidence as yet that invertebrates have such a system in the usual sense of the words, although recent studies by Cooper indicate that earthworms are able to reject cuticle grafts and to display a second-set phenomenon on repeat grafting. The fact that insects are about 100 times as resistant to the life-shortening effects of irradiation as are vertebrates might suggest a fundamental difference between the mechanisms of aging in these broad groups.

In conclusion it may be emphasized that the material outlined in Table 1 is certainly not exhaustive, and some of it may in fact not be appropriate. However, I suggest that this type of approach must be made in the construction of general hypotheses. It need hardly be pointed out that the various theories need not be mutually exclusive. Crosslinking might lead to somatic mutation and the latter could be expressed pathogenetically as immunogenetic diversification with an accompanying auto-immunity.

References

Alexander, P. and Connell, D. I. (1960). *Radiat. Res., 12,* 38–48.

Comfort, A. (1963). *Lancet, ii,* 138–140.

Connell, D. I. and Alexander, P. (1959). *Gerontologia, 3,* 153–158.

Cooper, E. L. personal communication.

Curtis, H. J. (1963). *Science, 141,* 686–694.

Dardeu, E. B., Jr. and Upton, A. C. (1964). *J. Geront., 19,* 62–65.

Fanestil, D. D. and Barrow, C. H., Jr. (1965). *J. Geront. 20,* 462–469.

Hildemann, W. H. (1957). *Ann. N.Y. Acad. Sci., 64,* 775–791.

Liu, R. and Walford, R. L. (1966). Submitted to *Nature.*

McCay, C. M. (1952). In *Cowdry's Problems of Aging,* 3rd ed., Lansing, A. L., Ed., Williams and Wilkins, New York, p. 139–202.

Suu, V. T. and Congdon, C. C. (1964). *Proc. Soc. Exp. Biol. Med., 116,* 825–829.

Troup, G. M., Wagner, I. and Walford, R. L. (1965). Unpublished observations.

Walford, R. L. (1962). *J. Geront., 17,* 281–285.

Walford, R. L. (1964). *Exp. Geront., 1,* 67–76.

Walford, R. L. (in press). In *Advances in Gerontological Research,* vol. 2, Strehler, B., Ed., Academic Press, New York.

Walford, R. L., Sjaarda, J. R. and Anderson, R. E. (1965). *Exp. Geront. 1,* 117–125.

DISCUSSION

DR. KOHN: Dr. Walford has provided a very arbitrary list. You can make a list with 150 items on it and someone is sure to say that item number 86 is trivial and has absolutely nothing to do with the major questions we are asking about an aging population. The questions I think have to be answered are why there is a specific life-span, an age related increase in probability of dying, a decrease in functional capacity of almost all physiologic and homeostatic processes. Whatever underlying mechanisms we are looking for has to be causally related to these manifestations of aging.

DR. MEDAWAR: The difference in life-span between different species should surely be included and this is one of the things that is most difficult to explain on an auto-immune basis. When comparing small animals like mice with large animals like elephants, some physiological performances are found to go at the same absolute rate in both of them. Others are more nearly in scale. One of the performances that goes at more or less the same absolute rate is an immunological process. The latent period of an immune reaction, its whole tempo, is very much the same in the two species. Nobody would deny that there might be a secular accumulation of auto-antibodies along with other degenerative changes, but how can you account for the cardinal fact of specific length of life on an auto-immunity basis?

DR. WALFORD: I certainly agree with Dr. Kohn's view that my list is arbitrary, but I insist that one must take this general approach, debatable as each specific point may be. One possible answer to Dr. Medawar is that the somatic mutation rate may be quite different for different species, as Failla has argued (*Ann. N.Y. Acad. Sci.,* 1958. *71,* 1124). If the somatic mutation rate is higher in mice, a more rapid immunogenetic diversification process would ensue.

DR. MEDAWAR: Supposing one could inject into an animal a drug which would erase all immunological memories, what would you predict would be the consequence of such an injection from the point of view of the animal's longevity?

DR. WALFORD: One might hope to prolong life-span by such a procedure. However, if immunogenetic mutations were involved, these would of course remain and the amelioration of an auto-immune aging process might merely be transitory.

DR. KOHN: We all talk as though by measuring life-span we are measuring aging. By some genetic selection or by some special treatment we change the life-span and believe we are interfering with aging processes. Unless we look at a natural population and understand what precedes death, what are the changes which lead to this end point, and then by some experimental procedure alter the rate of these same processes, we cannot draw conclusions regarding aging in natural populations.

DR. WALFORD: Workers in the irradiation field are faced with the problem of showing that radiation-induced shortening of life-span is or is not correlated with biochemical parameters of aging. Immunological experiment must proceed along the same lines. However, if one could significantly prolong natural life-span by an immunological technique, one would be justified in saying that he had interfered with the aging process. Experiments which merely shorten life-span are less easy to interpret.

DR. MAYNARD SMITH: Granted that there are some auto-immune diseases, is it clear whether these arise as a consequence of changes, mutational or otherwise, in an immunologically competent cell or in target cells, or do they arise as a consequence of mechanical or otherwise breaking down of barriers which were previously separating these cells? Is an intracellular event responsible or an organismic event?

DR. WALFORD: This important question cannot be answered on present evidence. Most students of auto-immunity believe that both processes are involved and dependent on the particular disease.

Author Index*

Alexander, P., 12, 14, *26,* 76, **77, 166,** *169*
Ames, S. R., 132, *139*
Anderson, R. E., 73, *74,* **166,** *169*
Angell, R., 92, *99*
Anton, E., 156, *157*
Ascheim, P., 128, *139*
Atwood, K. C., **32, 77, 80, 123**

Ballantyne, D. L., Jr., 137, *139*
Barness, L. A., 56, *60*
Barnett, C. H., 147
Barrow, C. H., Jr., 163, *169*
Bartlett, E. G., 96, *99*
Battips, D. M., 102, *116*
Becker, 118
Bender, M. A., 65, *74*
Bertini, F., 151, 152, *157*
Bhatnagar, P. L., 28, 54, *59*
Bidder, G. P., 83, *98*
Biggers, J. D., 131, *139*
Billingham, R. E., 137, *139*
Birren, J. E., **34, 61**
Blaha, G. C., 131, *139*
Blest, A. D., 8, *26*
Bondareff, W., 149, *157*
Bourne, G. H., **31, 60, 61, 142, 147,** 149, *157,* **158**
Bowler, K., 3, *26*
Boyd, W., 149, *157*
Brandes, D., **77,** 149, 151, 152, 156, *157*
Brandt, K. F., 46, 49, 51, 52, *59*
Bronowski, J., **75, 77, 78, 140, 141, 147, 148**
Brother Forsthoefel, 146
Brown, W. M. C., 131, *139*
Bruce, W. R., 91, *98*
Brunton, M., 131, *139*
Bryant, J. C., 101, *116*
Buchanan, J. M., 79

Buetow, D. E., 152, *157*
Bullough, W. S., 134, *139*
Burrows, M. T., 96, *98*

Calkins, G. N., 95, *98*
Carrel, A., 83, 86, 96, *98*
Casarett, G. W., 79
Castor, L. N., 101, *116*
Chadwick, L. E., 56, *59*
Chesterman, F. C., 126, *139*
Cieciura, S. J., 96, *100,* 101, *116*
Clark, A. M., 15, *26,* 43, 48, 50–52, 55, *59*
Clarke, J. M., 20, 25, *26*
Clausen, J. J., 112, *116*
Clegg, J. S., 56, 57, *59*
Cohn, A. E., 96, *99*
Comfort, A., 83, 95, *99,* 163, *169*
Congdon, C. C., 168, *169*
Connell, D. I., 12, 14, *26,* **166,** *169*
Converse, J. M., 137, *139*
Cooper, E. L., 168, *169*
Court Brown, W. M., 92, *99*
Cowdry, E. V., 83, *99*
Crowley, C., 65–67, 69–71, *74,* 92, *99,* 138, *139*
Cruickshank, C. N. D., 133, *139*
Cudkowicz, G., 90, *99*
Curtis, H. J., 10, 13, 14, *26,* **29,** 63, 65–72, *74,* **74–78, 80,** 92, 99, **123,** 138, *139,* **142,** 166, 169

Danielli, J. F., 9, *26,* 95, *99*
Dardeu, E. B., Jr., 166, *169*
Dauer, M., 28
De Duve, C., 149, 151–154, *157*
DeOme, K. B., 90, *99,* 126, *139*
DeRobertis, E. D. P., 149, *157*
Deszi, I. D., 158
Dethier, V. G., 56, *59*
Doll, R., 92, *99*

---

* *Italic* numerals indicate pages carrying full bibliographic listings; **boldface** numerals indicate discussion participation.

Dulbecco, R., 35, 75, 76, 79, 87, 100, 120
Dunham, L. J., 91, 100

Earle, W. R., 84, 99, 101, 116, 117
Ebeling, A. H., 83, 84, 99
Enders, J. F., 87, 100
Enquist, I. F., 136, 139
Evans, D. R., 56, 57, 59
Everett, N. B., 94, 99

Failla, G., 10, 26, 170
Fallon, J. F., 162
Falzone, J. A., 34
Fanestil, D. D., 163, 169
Filch, S. M., 132, 139
Filler, M., 137, 139
Finn, C. A., 131, 132, 139
Fischer, A., 101, 116
Fisher, H. W., 101, 102, 116
Foà, C., 126, 139
Foley, G. E., 86, 99
Ford, C. E., 90, 99, 102, 116
Franks, L. M., 126, 139
Friedman, S., 57, 59
Frueh, B., 136, 139
Fuller, M., 66, 67, 74

Gallop, P. M., 120
Gasseling, M. T., 160, 161
Gee, M. V., 154, 157, 157
Geiringer, E., 126, 139
Gey, G. O., 84, 99
Gey, M. K., 84, 99
Gilmour, D., 56, 59
Glaser, D. A., 28, 37, 38–40, 117, 123, 142
Glinos, A. D., 96, 99
Gooch, C. P., 65, 74
Goodlin, R. C., 130, 139, 140, 141
Gray, S. M., 90, 99
Green, H., 86, 100
Grobstein, C., 32, 117, 162
Gross, J., 5, 26, 32, 35, 143
Guthrie, G. D., 79

Halber, J. A., 137, 139
Ham, R. G., 103, 104, 106, 107, 116
Hamburger, V., 160, 161

Hamerton, J. L., 92, 99
Hamilton, H. L., 160, 161
Handler, A. H., 86, 99
Harkness, R. C., 132, 139
Harrison, G. A., 126, 139
Harvey, S. C., 96, 99
Hastings, A. B., 80
Hawkins, 57, 58
Hayflick, L., 9, 10, 26, 65, 74, 83–89, 96, 99, 103, 116, 117, 119, 120, 121, 122, 123, 136, 138, 139, 148
Held, W., 161, 161
Hewett, C. L., 134, 139
Hildemann, W. H., 138, 139, 166, 169
Hollingsworth, M. J., 3, 26
Hood, S. L., 96, 99
Howden, G. F., 56, 59
Howes, E. L., 96, 99
Hsu, T. C., 101, 102, 116
Hughes, W. L., 90, 99
Hungerford, D. A., 102, 116

Jacob, F., 17, 26
Jacobs, P. A., 92, 99, 131, 139
Jacquemont, C., 112, 116
Jennings, H. S., 95, 99
Jensen, F., 87, 99
Jones, E. C., 131, 139, 142
Jones, H. B., 7, 26

Kalf, G. F., 56, 60
Kay, H. E. M., 93, 94, 99
Kilby, B. A., 56, 59
Kohn, R. R., 27–31, 34, 39, 61, 79, 119, 123, 141, 147, 148, 157, 158, 170
Koprowski, H., 87, 99
Krohn, P. L., 4, 27, 65, 74, 75, 91, 99, 125–131, 133, 136, 139, 140–143, 146–148, 159
Kupelwieser, E. B., 86, 100

Lamb, M. J., 16–18, 27, 29
Lawrence, E. B., 134, 139
Leitch, A., 138, 139
Leith, J., 66, 68, 74
Levenbook, L., 44, 59
Lieberman, H. S., 45, 46, 59

Likely, G. D., 101, *117*
Lindop, P. J., 10, 11, *27*, 68, *74*
Liu, R., 166, *169*
Ludwig, M. I., 132, *139*
Lyon, M., 16, *27*

Marcus, P. I., 96, *100*, 101, *116*
Mark, D. D., 154, *157*, 157
Mathivon, M. F., 112, *116*
Mawdsley, R., 126, *139*
Maynard Smith, J., 1, 4, 8, 17, 20, 21, *26*, 27, *27–32*, **35**, **38**, **60**, **75**, **76**, 83, *99*, **120**, **170**
McCay, M. M., 163, 168, *169*
McClaren, A., 131, *139*
McCulloch, E. A., 90, 91, *100*, 101, *116*, 118, 119
McDonald, W. C., 94, *99*
McGuire, V. M., 92, *99*
Medawar, P. B., 4, *27*, **30**, **38**, 83, *99*, **121**, **140–143**, **146**, **147**, **161**, **169**, **170**
Medina, D., 87, *100*
Meeker, B. E., 91
Melander, Y., 112, *116*
Mellman, W. J., 102, *116*
Micklem, H. S., 90, *99*
Mildvan, A. S., 154, *157*, 157
Mintz, B., 159, *161*
Moertel, C. G., 94, *100*
Monod, J., 17, *26*
Moore, A. E., 85, *100*, 101, 102, *116*
Moorhead, P. S., 84–88, 96, *99*, 101, 102, *116*, 121
Morkovin, D., 96, *100*
Muggleton, A., 9, *26*, 95, *99*
Muller, H. J., 83, *99*
Mundy, J., 133, *139*
Murray, H. A., 96, *99*

Norris, G., 96, *99*
Novikoff, A. B., 152, *157*
Nowell, P. C., 102, *116*
Nowinski, W. W., 149, *157*

Orgel, L. E., 24, *27*, **39**, **60**, **75**, **77**, **122**, **158**

Parker, F. C., 101, *116*

Parker, R. C., 83, 86, *99*, *100*
Parker, R. F., 102, *117*
Pearl, R., 83, *99*
Penrose, L. S., 140
Pepper, F. J., 126, *139*
Perry, K., 34
Pontén, J. A., 87, *99*
Prudden, J. F., 136, *139*
Prunierias, M., 112, *116*
Puck, T. T., **38–40**, **76**, **79**, **80**, 81, 96, *100*, 101–104, 106, 107, **112**, *116*, *117*, **117**, **120**, **123**

Quimby, M. C., 86, *100*

Ravdin, R. G., 87, *99*
Reitemeier, R. J., 94, *100*
Rhoads, C. P., 86, *100*
Ritossa, 33
Rizet, G., 95, *100*
Roberts, R. C., 91, *100*
Robinson, A., 101, 102, *116*
Rockstein, M., **28**, **29**, 43, 45–52, 54, 55, 58, *59*, **60**, **61**, *139*
Roman, L., 141
Rotblat, J., 10, 11, *27*, 68, *74*
Rothfels, K. H., 86, *100*
Rubin, M. A., 15, *26*
Rubinstein, D., **74**

Sabo, J. C., 136, *139*
Sacher, G. A., 5, *27*, 28
Sachs, L., 87, *100*
Sacktor, B., 44, *59*
Saez, F. A., 149, *157*
Sahinen, F. M., 132, *139*
Saksela, E., 87, *99*
Salk, J., **60**
Sallman, B., **40**, **61**, **79**
Samis, H. V., Jr., 34
Sanford, K. K., 101, *117*
Sang, 35
Sato, G., 102, *116*
Saunders, J. W., Jr., 159–161, *161*, **161**, **162**
Saunders, L. C., 160, *161*
Sawant, P. L., 158
Sawyer, W. H., 56, *60*
Schilling, E. L., 101, *116*

Schlyen, S. M., 91, *100*
Schneller, M., 9, *27*
Shearer, G. M., 90, *99*
Shein, H. M., 87, *100*
Shorter, R. G., 94, *100*
Silverstone, H., 67, *74*
Siminovitch, L., 90, 91, *100*, 119
Sinex, F. M., **35, 60, 75–79**
Sjaarda, J. R., 73, *74*, 166, *169*
Smith, E. W., 151, *157*
Snell, K. C., 91, *100*
Soderwall, A. L., 132, *139*
Sonneborn, T. M., 9, 23, *27*, 90, 95, *100*
Southam, C. M., 85, *100*, 101, *116*
Spiegelman, 33
Steffen, J., 107, *117*
Stern, H., **76**
Sternberg, S., 101, *116*
Stevenson, K. G., 66, 69, *74*
Stewart, H. L., 91, *100*
Stockwell, R. A., 147
Strehler, B. L., 11, *27*, 95, *100*, **117, 120, 142, 148,** 154, *157*, **157, 158**
Strong, L. C., 87, *100*, **141, 143, 146**
Sumner, J. B., 47
Suu, V. T., 168, *169*
Svaha, D., 136, *139*
Swim, H. E., 102, *117*
Syverton, J. T., 112, *116*
Szilard, L., 10, *27*, 72, *74*, 79

Talbert, G. B., 129, 130, *139*
Tannenbaum, A., 67, *74*

Tappel, A. L., 158
Taylor, A. I., 92, *99*
Teneick, M. L., 136, *139*
Thoenen, H., 96, *100*
Thung, 75
Till, J., **76, 79,** 90, 91, *100*, **118,** 119, 157
Tilley, J., 66–68, 70, 71, *74*
Titus, J. L., 94, *100*
Tjio, J. H., 102–104, *117*
Todaro, G. J., 86, *100*
Trier, J. S., 94, *99*
Troup, G. M., 166, 168, *169*

Upton, A. C., 90, *99*, 166, *169*

Verzar, F., 5, *27*, 96, *100*
Vogt, M., **75,** 87, *100*

Wagner, I., 166, 168, *169*
Walford, R. L., 73, *74*, **75, 80,** 138, *139*, **143,** 163, 164, 166, 168, *169*, **169, 170**
Watanabe, M. I., 44, *59*
Wigglesworth, V. B., 44, 56, *60*
Wilcox, H. H., 149, *157*
William-Ashman, H. G., 154, *157*
Williams, C. M., **40,** 44, 45, 56, *59, 60*, **80, 120**
Williams, G. C., 4, *27*
Williams, M. V., 44, 45, *60*
Wolf, K., 86, *100*
Wulff, V. J., **34, 35, 117**
Wyatt, G. R., 56, *60*

Subject Index

Accelerated aging, 155
Acetyl cholinesterase, 47
Adenine nucleotide, 150
ADP, 49
Age, chimaeras, 90
  adrenal cortex, 126
  bone, 126
  mammary gland, 126
  orthotopic ovarian, 127–129, 131–132
  prostate, 126
  skin, 133–138
  thymus, 126
Aging, definition of, 30–32, 38
  distinction from senescence, 31, 159
  insects, 43–59
  pigments, 149, 154, 155, 157, 158
  precocious versus accelerated, 29
  radiation specific, 31
Aging changes, cellular processes in
    8–10
  general classification of, 6–9
Aging theories, clinker, 165
  crosslinking, 165
  denaturation, 165
  immunological, 165
  somatic mutation, 165
Alpha glycerophosphate dehydrogenase,
    51, 52, 53, 56
Amoebae, 9
AMP, 19
Antibiotics, 7
Apis mellifera, lifespan of, 43
ATP, in insect flight muscle, 48
ATPase, activity in rat muscle, 50
  after de-alation, 53
  in fly flight muscle, 48, 50, 51,
    53, 56
Atresia, of oocytes, 127
Auto-immune disease, 168, 169, 170
Autoimmunity, 79
Autophagic vacuoles, 152
  effect of X-rays on, 152

Bacteria, aging of, 37, 38, 40, 41, 123
Blastocysts, transfer of, in mice and
    hamsters, 130, 131, 141
Body size, brain size, and longevity, 5
Brain, changes in enzymes, 47
Brown atrophy of heart, pigment in, 149

Capillary fibrosis, 30, 73, 79, 141
Cartilage, effect on QO_2 of skin grafts,
    135, 136, 147, 148
Cell death, 8
  during development, 161
  in embryos, 159–161
Cell kinetics, 93
Cell lines, definition of, 85, 86, 87
Cell loss, 73
Cell monolayers, characteristics of, 104
Cell preservation, 96, 97, 88, 89, 121
Cell strains, definition of, 84
  infected with virus, 87
  storage at low temperatures, 88, 89
Cell types, requirements for cultures of,
    102, 103, 104
Cellular aging, 64
Chick cells, lifespan in culture, 83
Chromosomal aberrations, 13, 14, 92
  in liver, and age, 65, 67–69, 76, 78, 80
  and irradiation, 69, 70, 71
Chromosomal abnormalities in blasto-
    cysts, 130
Chromosomes, repair of damage to, 71
Clonal aging, 9, 23, 32
Collagen, 5, 6, 13, 73, 165
  produced by cultures, 96

De-alation, 54
Deterioration of the uterine environ-
    ment, 129, 132
Diet, 67
DNA, 4, 33, 79
  copying errors in cell strains, 89
  synthesis, in chick embryos, 161

Dog, age changes in liver, 66
Dominant mutation, 16, 17
    See also Mutation; Recessive mutation;
    Somatic mutation
Drosophila, 2, 3, 14, 15, 16, 17, 18, 19,
    21, 25
    comparative radiosensitivity of
        male and female, 19
    lifespan at varying temperatures, 21
    lifespan after X-rays, 18
    lifetables of, 3

Environmental stress, 8
Enzymes, 47
    activating, 24, 25
Ethyl methane sulfonate (EMS), 14
Euglena, effect of starvation on, 152

Fibrillar muscle, 44
Flight muscle, mitochondria, 54, 55, 56
Force of mortality, 1
    measurement of, 2

Generation time, of cultures, 107
Genes and chromosomal stability, 67
Germ cells, mutations, 25
Giant mitochondria, 44, 45, 54, 56
Gompertz plot, 2
Growth capacity, in culture, 96

Habrobracon, 15, 16, 17
Hematopoietic cells, proliferative
    ability of, 90, 118, 119
Hepatomas, in mice, 166
Histo-incompatibility reactions in aging,
    164
    temperature dependence in gold fish,
    166
Homeostatic mechanisms, 164
House flies, age changes in wings of,
    46, 46, 47, 60
    age of wing loss in, 47, 48, 49
    survival curves, 45, 46
Human diploid cell strains, karyotype,
    92

Immunological parameters and aging,
    168
Immunological tolerance, 7

Immunosuppresive agents and life span,
    167, 170
Implantation sites, 132
Imuran and life span, 167
Insects, 43, 44
    aging changes in flight muscle, 8, 15,
    17, 19, 44, 54, 56
Intramitochondrial magnesium activated
    ATPase activity, 48, 50, 51, 53, 54, 55

Karyotype, 101, 102
    abnormalities in rabbit, after culture,
    112, 113, 114, 115

Lifespan, age pigment in, 165
    changes in collagen, 165
    and diet, 165
    of diploids and triploids, 17
    DNA, 165
    effect of irradiation, 165, 166
    effect of temperature, 165
    at varying temperatures, 21
Life tables, aging deduced from, 29
Lipofuscin, 149, 158
Lipolytic enzymes in autophagic vac-
    uoles, 153
Liver, 67–71
Liver enzymes, in aging mice, 167
Longevity, correlated with brain size
    and body size, 5
    species specificity, 27
Lysosomes and aging, 149–156, 158, 161
    and cell death, 151
Lysozymes, renal, 168

Malignancy, in cultures, 103
Maternal age, influence of, 140, 144, 145,
    146
Mice, age changes in liver, 65, 66, 67
    reproductive function and age, 126–132
Microorganisms, aging of, 37, 39
Mitochondria, in insect flight, 54, 55, 56
Mitotic figures, in aging liver, 66
Molecular aging, 5
Mongolism, 127, 140
Morphogenetic death, 161
mRNA, 15, 24, 26
Muscular dystrophy-like syndrome, in
    rats, 50, 61
Mutagen, 13, 14

Mutation, aging effect of, 72, 73
Mutation theory of aging, limitations, 71, 72
Myleran, 14, 16

Natural selection, 2, 3, 4, 6, 8, 9
Nervous system, 7
Neutron irradiation, 70, 80
Nucleic acids, 4, 23

Oocytes, atresia of, 127, 142
  and hormones, 142, 143
  loss of and hypophysectomy, 142, 143
Organelles, 9, 10
Ovary, orthotopic transplantation of, 127–129, 131, 132

Paramecia, 9, 23, 95
Programmed death, 8, 27, 28, 160
Prolongation of life, by irradiation, 28
Prostatic cells, autophagic vacuoles and hormones, 152
Protein synthesis, rate of, 22, 23, 34
Protozoa, immortality of, 94, 95

QO₂ in skin normal mouse, 133–135
  effect of cartilage, 135–136
  influence of age, 133–135
  in transplanted skin, 134–138

Radiation and aging, 10, 12, 17, 19, 22, 29, 30, 68–71, 76, 77
Radiomimetic drugs, effects of, 166
Rate of living theory, 73
Recessive mutations, 15, 16
  See also Mutation
Residual bodies, 152, 153
Ribosomes, 21, 22, 32, 33
RNA, 26, 33, 34, 79
  in embryos, 161

Sarcosomes, 44
Senile amyloidosis, 75, 166
Single cell plating, technique for, 105, 106
Skin, cancer in, 138
  mitotic abnormalities, 138
  QO₂ of, 133
  revascularization of, 137
  serial transplantation of, 91, 136–138
  viability of, 137
Somatic mutation, 9, 10–13, 15, 16, 17, 24, 63–74, 80, 87
  See also Mutation
Stem cells, 93, 94, 103, 119, 120
Synchronization of aging changes, 4, 5

Temperature, effect on drosophila aging, 17, 19, 20, 21
Tendon, 6
Tissue cultures, 83–98
  changes with age of donor, 89, 96, 117, 122, 123
  finite lifespan of, 87, 90, 92, 93, 122
  long term growth of mammalian cells in, 101–116
  minimal growth requirements of, 104
  of skin, 102, 105
  technique, 102–104
Thiamine, 56, 57, 58
Transplantation, and age changes in reproduction, 126–132
  and aging of skin, 133, 138
Trehalase, 56
Trehalose, 56, 57

Uterus, 132

Vitamin E, 132

7